Total English

PRE-INTERMEDIATE

Workbook with Key

PEARSON
Longman

Antonia Clare and JJ Wilson
with Will Moreton

Contents

Vocabulary | everyday actions

1 Match a verb from A with a word or phrase from B.

A	B
1 read	a a bus
2 listen	b to bed late
3 get up	c on the phone
4 stay	d early
5 go	e your emails
6 chat	f nothing
7 watch	g in bed late
8 check	h to the radio
9 do	i TV
10 take	j a magazine

2 Complete the sentences with the missing verbs.

1 She _____ her emails when she gets to work in the morning.
2 We _____ in on Saturday nights – we don't like going clubbing.
3 I normally _____ the train at 9.00 a.m.
4 Do you ever _____ a lie-in on Saturday morning?
5 I _____ for a swim on Saturdays.
6 I like to _____ a nap after lunch.
7 What newspaper does he _____ ?
8 They usually _____ their friends over for dinner on Friday evenings.
9 He _____ to the radio in the car on the way to work.
10 I always _____ the shopping on the way home from work.

Reading

3 a Read the text quickly and match the headings in the box to the correct time of day.

> Eat your dinner   Stretch
> Think about a problem   Visit the dentist

A time for everything ...

What is the right time of day for your body to do everything?

Noon _____
Your brain works best at around midday. It's a good time to talk to your boss about a problem or do a difficult crossword.

2 p.m. _____
Do you hate going to the dentist? Make an appointment in the early afternoon. You don't feel pain so badly at this time of day.

5 p.m. _____
Are you very hungry when you finish work? This is because food tastes better in the early evening. Eating late is a bad idea. After midnight it is more difficult for our bodies to process fat, and this can give you heart problems.

8 p.m. _____
The best time to do exercise is around 8 p.m. At this time our body temperature is at its maximum, so our muscles are warmer.

b Read the text again. Mark the sentences true (T) or false (F).

1 Your brain works best in the middle of the day.
2 The best time to do a crossword is early morning.
3 It's a good idea to go to the dentist between 1 and 3 p.m.
4 Food tastes good in the early evening. This makes you hungry.
5 The best time to eat dinner is just before you go to bed.
6 It is good to do exercise in the evening because your muscles are warm.

New Total English
Pre-Intermediate Workbook 2011
Pearson Longman

Grammar | likes and dislikes

4 **a** Complete the texts with words from the boxes.

> hate   keen   like   love   ~~stand~~

Andreas (26)
Germany

'I can't <u>stand</u> doing nothing. I really (1) _____ holidays where people lie on the beach all day – I can't understand it. I absolutely (2) _____ doing exercise so I get up early every day and run for ten kilometres before breakfast. I'm not very (3) _____ on team sports like football. When I go on holiday, I do water-sports like surfing and sailing. I quite (4) _____ walking and cycling too!'

> like   love   mind   quite   stand

Seung Ah (24)
South Korea

'I absolutely (5) _____ eating good food. Cooking is very important in my culture. Usually my mother and my grandmother do all the cooking. They don't (6) _____ doing this but sometimes I (7) _____ helping them too. I can't (8) _____ fast food, especially hamburgers, but I do (9) _____ like Italian food, like pizza!'

b 🔘 2 Listen and check your answers.

5 Complete the sentences with one word from the box.

> ~~absolutely~~   can't   keen (x2)   like
> mind   really

I *absolutely* love playing tennis.

1 I'm not very _____ on watching TV because there are so many bad programmes.
2 She doesn't _____ going to the cinema if it is an action film. It can be fun!
3 I'm quite _____ on sports in general but especially football.
4 He _____ stand boxing – he hates to watch people hit each other.
5 I _____ like reading, especially novels.
6 I quite _____ going to the theatre but it's very expensive.

6 Put the words in the correct order to make sentences.

1 love going museums to they absolutely.
2 he works having the radio doesn't he mind on while.
3 like early getting she doesn't up.
4 eating out at I like weekends.
5 we like together working quite.
6 quite she's keen gymnastics on.
7 not we're very on dancing keen.
8 really sports hates she.
9 can't I playing stand chess.

Vocabulary | going out

7 Complete the sentences with *go*, *go to* or *go on*. You may need to change the form of the verb.

I don't like *going to* musicals.

1 I usually _____ clubbing on Saturday night with my friends.
2 I absolutely love _____ the theatre.
3 I never _____ concerts. I prefer listening to music at home.
4 You don't _____ bowling very often, do you?
5 I sometimes _____ ice skating at the weekend.
6 My mother always _____ a guided tour of the cities she visits on holiday.
7 Whenever a new Brad Pitt film comes out I _____ the cinema to see it.
8 My brother works in a museum so I _____ the exhibitions for free.

Listening

1 **a** 🔘 3 Cover the audioscript. Listen and make notes in the table.

	Sleep weekdays (hours)	Sleep weekend (hours)	Insomnia (yes/no)	Alarm clock (yes/no)
Liz				
Paul				

b Answer the questions.

1 Who is always tired?

_____.

2 Who likes to stay in bed late on Sundays?

_____.

3 Who has problems sleeping when they are worried?

_____.

4 What happens to Liz when she drinks a lot of coffee?

_____.

5 Why does Liz use two alarm clocks?

_____.

6 When does Paul use an alarm clock?

_____.

AUDIOSCRIPT

Interviewer: So, how many hours do you sleep, Liz?

Liz: Not enough. I usually sleep about six hours on weekdays. That's why I'm always tired.

Interviewer: And you, Paul?

Paul: I get seven or eight hours sleep on weekdays. It depends what time I go to bed.

Interviewer: What about weekends?

Liz: Oh, I get more sleep at weekends – about ten hours. Sometimes I don't get up until lunchtime!

Paul: Really? I can't stay in bed that long. I usually sleep a bit less at weekends, about an hour less. Sometimes I try to stay in bed but then I just get up and start doing things in the house.

Interviewer: Did you know that ten percent of the population suffer from insomnia – when you can't fall asleep. Do you ever get that?

Paul: Yeah, sometimes. When I'm worried about work.

Interviewer: And you, Liz?

Liz: No. I don't usually have any problems falling asleep. Very occasionally, I can't sleep if I've drunk too much coffee.

Paul: Yes, drinking coffee is a bad idea.

Interviewer: And do you use an alarm clock to wake up in the morning?

Liz: Absolutely. Yes. I can't wake up without an alarm clock. In fact, I have two because I turn the first alarm clock off, and fall asleep again.

Paul: I don't need an alarm clock usually. Sometimes I use one if I have to get up very early, to catch an aeroplane or something.

Vocabulary | describing your day and lifestyle

2 **a** Match the words (1–8) with their definitions (a–h).

1 boring
2 busy
3 fun
4 exciting
5 lazy
6 relaxing
7 stressful
8 unusual

a lots of time to do nothing
b something which makes you feel calm
c not interesting
d occupied with lots of things to do
e strange or different
f enjoyable
g interesting and stimulating
h something which makes you worry a lot

b Complete the sentences with the correct adjective from exercise 2a.

I think maths is really *boring*. I fell asleep in class last week.

1 My job is really _____. I have so many things to worry about.

2 He's a(n) _____ person. He acts in such a strange way.

3 I like _____ hobbies like painting and listening to classical music.

4 He has a really _____ lifestyle because he's not working at the moment.

5 The new Harry Potter film is so _____ - it's got lots of action.

6 He's very _____ – he's got a lot of work at the moment.

7 I love playing cards with friends. It's great _____.

Grammar | Present Simple; adverbs of frequency

3 Complete the sentences using the correct form of the verbs in brackets.

Sylvie _studies_ (study) French at university. She (1) _____ (not know) what she wants to do when she (2) _____ (finish) her degree. Sylvie (3) _____ (live) at home with her family.

Max (4) _____ (work) in the city. He (5) _____ (have) a new sports car, and a big house. He (6) _____ (enjoy) going out and spending lots of money. He (7) _____ (not smoke) and he (8) _____ (do) a lot of exercise in the gym.

Albert (9) _____ (not work). He's 75 years old. He usually (10) _____ (spend) his time at home. He (11) _____ (watch) TV and (12) _____ (read) the newspaper. Sometimes he (13) _____ (go) for a walk or (14) _____ (do) some shopping. He (15) _____ (not cook), so his daughter (16) _____ (bring) him food to eat.

4 Write the questions for these answers.

A: _Where do you live?_
B: I live in Madrid.

1 A: _____?
   B: I have breakfast at about 10 o'clock on Saturdays.
2 A: _____?
   B: They work outside London.
3 A: _____?
   B: She goes to the gym once a week.
4 A: _____?
   B: On Friday night I often go out.
5 A: _____?
   B: No, they never go clubbing.

5 Put the words in the correct order to make sentences.

1 to books take my I ever forget to hardly college.
   _____.
2 in school the is never late for morning Jake.
   _____.
3 see Pablo after and Juan we often the game.
   _____.
4 drink the coffee do you always in mornings?
   _____.
5 visit in my we sometimes grandmother France.
   _____.

Pronunciation | do/does

6 a 🔊 4 Listen and write the questions you hear.

1 A: _____?
   Your answer: _____.
2 A: _____?
   Your answer: _____.
3 A: _____?
   Your answer: _____.
4 A: _____?
   Your answer: _____.
5 A: _____?
   Your answer: _____.
6 A: _____?
   Your answer: _____.

b Now write answers that are true for you on the lines under the questions.

c Listen again. Underline the stressed form of _do/does/don't_ or _doesn't_ in the questions. Practise saying the questions and the answers.

Grammar | Present Continuous: now and around now

1 Answer the questions about each picture. Write sentences.

Does he teach? _Yes, he does._
Is he teaching now? _No, he isn't._
What is he doing? _He's painting his house._

1   Does he manage a bank? _____.
    Is he working now? _____.
    What is he doing? _____.

2   Do they play guitar? _____.
    Are they playing guitar now? _____.
    What are they doing? _____.

3   Does she study French? _____.
    Is she studying French now? _____.
    What is she doing? _____.

2 Write answers to the questions that are true for you. Write complete sentences.

What are you doing at the moment?
I'm studying English at the moment.

1   Are you watching TV now?
    _____.

2   What time do you start English class?
    _____.

3   Are you learning another language?
    _____.

4   Do you study English every day?
    _____.

5   Are you looking for a job at the moment?
    _____.

6   Do you play football on Saturdays?
    _____.

7   Do you like Indian food?
    _____.

3 Complete the email by choosing the correct form of the verb.

From: Jo

To: Gloria

1 Hello Gloria
   How are things in Canada? I hope you
   are well. Here everything (1) *changes/is
   changing*. Juan and I got married, and
5 we (2) *start/are starting* a new business
   too. It's very exciting! We (3) *open/are
   opening* an Indian restaurant in the
   city centre called Juan's. Everyone
   (4) *loves/is loving* Indian food but there
10 are no restaurants here at the moment.
   We are opening next month, so we
   (5) *are/are being* really busy looking for
   staff. (6) *It's/It's being* very difficult to
   find good waiters. What about you?
15 (7) *Are you working/Do you work* hard at
   the moment? Write and tell me.
   Hope to hear from you soon.
   Take care,
   Paola

Vocabulary | time phrases

4 Complete the sentences with the correct prepositions.

Mina

She gets up *at* 11 o'clock every day.

1 _____ the afternoon she watches TV.

2 _____ about 8 p.m. she has a pizza at home.

3 _____ Saturdays she stays at home chatting on the phone.

Dan

4 _____ the summer, he goes to the beach to meet people.

5 He always goes out with friends _____ the evenings.

6 _____ weekends, he goes to parties or out to the cinema.

Sofia

7 _____ the mornings she reads the newspaper.

8 _____ Mondays she always goes to a museum.

9 _____ lunchtime she likes going to art galleries.

Reading

5 Read the text. Mark the sentences true (T) or false (F).

eBay is an Internet webpage where people buy and sell almost anything at any time of day or night. Millions of people all round the world use eBay to find telephones and clothes, computers and cars.

How does it work? Imagine you want to buy a camera on eBay. You enter the keyword 'camera' and the type of camera you want. When you see the camera you like, you click on it to see a picture. If you decide you want to buy the camera you enter the amount of money you want to pay. This is called a bid. If your bid is the highest one, you get the camera. There is also a 'Buy it Now' price. If you pay the Buy it Now price, there are no more bids and you get the camera. The person who sells the camera sends it directly to you.

If it is easy to buy things on eBay, it is easy to sell things too. Lots of people sell their old computer when they get a new one. When children grow and their clothes are too small for them, parents often sell the clothes on eBay. In fact, you can sell anything you want. Some people even open their own 'eBay shop' where they sell lots of different things. The best thing about eBay? You don't have to be a computer expert to use it.

1 On eBay you can shop 24 hours a day.
2 If you pay the 'Buy it Now' price other people can continue making bids.
3 Selling on eBay is complicated.
4 Parents often sell their children's clothes on eBay.
5 It is possible to open your own eBay shop.
6 You need to be an expert to use eBay.

New Total English Pre-Int. Workbook 2011 Pearson Longman

2 Music

Vocabulary | music

1 Put the underlined letters in the correct order to make a word.

1 Bach is my favourite classical <u>pomcoser</u>.
2 That song is the new <u>ngsile</u> from his latest album.
3 I bought the <u>racsotundk</u> to the film because I loved the music.
4 They are going to play five <u>crcoents</u> in South America this summer.
5 The song was at the top of the <u>crthas</u> for three weeks.

2 Match the sentence halves (1–6) to (a–f).

1 I like heavy
2 She's really
3 I can read
4 There is a great theme
5 The band's lead
6 The song got to the top

a music because I studied violin when I was a child.
b song at the start of the film.
c singer left. They're looking for a new one.
d metal, especially groups like Metallica.
e of the charts at Christmas.
f into reggae. She's a big fan of Bob Marley.

3 Compete the dialogue with the words from the box. You may need to change the form of a verb.

> download   duet   flop   lyrics
> soundtrack

A: Have you heard the (1) _____ to the new vampire film, *Dawnings*?
B: Yeah, I (2) _____ it from the Internet the other day. There's a great (3) _____ by Flint and James Barry. They sing really well together.
A: Flint's last album didn't sell well at all. It was a complete (4) _____ .
B: I know. The songs were different from his usual material.
A: I agree. Did you listen to the (5) _____ ? They didn't have any meaning to them at all.

Grammar | Past Simple

4 Complete the facts with the correct verbs from the boxes in the Past Simple.

> appear   be   have   marry   sell   sing   win   write

The Queen of Pop

1 Madonna _____ with a group called Breakfast Club when she was young.
2 *Everybody* _____ Madonna's first hit in 1982.
3 Madonna _____ actor Sean Penn in 1985.
4 She _____ in the film *Desperately Seeking Susan* in the same year.
5 She _____ a Golden Globe for the film *Evita*.
6 Madonna's album *Music* _____ four million copies in ten days.
7 Madonna _____ her first child in 1996.
8 Madonna _____ a book for children called *The English Roses*.

> buy   make   marry   open   own   sell   win   work

The King of Rock and Roll

1 Elvis _____ the first ever music video: *Jailhouse Rock*.
2 Elvis once _____ a pet chimpanzee called Scatter.
3 He _____ as a lorry driver before becoming a singer.
4 Elvis _____ Priscilla in 1967.
5 His hit *Heartbreak Hotel* _____ 300,000 copies the first week.
6 Elvis was called the *King of Rock & Roll* but he only ever _____ a Grammy for his gospel music.
7 Elvis _____ his famous Graceland mansion in 1957.
8 In 1982, Elvis' ex-wife Priscilla _____ Graceland to the public.

Pre-Int. Workbook Total English
A. Clare, J.J. Wilson, W. Moreton 2011

5 Write the questions for the answers, using the prompts.

A: (Where/be/last night?) _Where were you last night?_
B: I was at home studying.

1 A: (What/have/for lunch/yesterday?) _____ ?
  B: I had a salad.
2 A: (What/do/Saturday night?) _____ ?
  B: I went out with some friends.
3 A: (What time/get up/this morning?) _____ ?
  B: I got up at half past six.
4 A: (What time/leave/house/this morning?) _____ ?
  B: I left the house at eight o'clock.
5 A: (newspaper/read/Sunday?) _____ ?
  B: I read _The Sunday Times._

6 Laura works in the music industry. Look at a list of the things she wanted to do yesterday. Write sentences to say what she did and didn't do.

meet Bob for lunch ✓

finish report on the concert locations ✗

meet with marketing representatives ✓

take suit to the cleaners ✗

ring Shane to organise party ✓

talk to producers about the CD cover ✗

check concert dates ✓

organise accommodation for the journalists ✓

pay the video company ✓

talk to the sound engineers ✓

She met Bob for lunch.
She didn't finish the report on the concert locations.

1 _____ .
2 _____ .
3 _____ .
4 _____ .
5 _____ .
6 _____ .
7 _____ .
8 _____ .

Pronunciation | -ed

7 **a** 🔊 5 Listen and repeat the sentences.

1 I <u>worked</u> in the library when I was at college.
2 When I was a boy my mum always <u>kissed</u> me goodnight before I went to sleep.
3 I <u>wanted</u> to be a dentist when I was young.
4 He <u>finished</u> his studies in 1998.
5 They <u>moved</u> to Korea when they got married.
6 Her schooldays <u>ended</u> in 2006.
7 I <u>waited</u> for a few years after finishing university to buy a house.
8 I <u>loved</u> playing tennis when I was at school.
9 My parents really <u>believed</u> in me when I was a teenager.

b Put the underlined verbs into the correct column according to the pronunciation of -ed.

/t/	/d/	/ɪd/
worked		

c Add three more verbs to each column.

How to... | refer to past times

8 **a** Complete the sentences with the correct words from the box.

after   ago   later   last   in   in the   when

a Six weeks _____ I sold my business for $2 million.
b _____ mid 1990s I graduated from university with a degree in music.
c _____ I was a teenager I played four musical instruments.
d _____ working for two years in my old university I started my own business making musical instruments.
e I left school _____ 1990.
f _____ year I decided I wanted to stop working.
g A year _____ I started working in my old university.

b Put the events in order to make a life story.

1 ___ 2 ___ 3 ___ 4 ___ 5 ___ 6 ___
7 ___

Grammar | Present Perfect Simple: experience

1 Choose the correct alternative.

A: Nick, tell us about your career.

B: (1) *I've made/I was made* twenty-two CDs and (2) *I've perform/I've performed* for the President many times.

A: Fantastic.

B: And (3) *I's won/I've won* eighteen awards.

A: How many records (4) *you have sold/have you sold*?

B: (5) *I've sold/I'm sold* about 50 million.

A: (6) *Has you/Have you* ever wanted to do a different job?

B: No. I was born to be a rock star.

A: On your new CD, (7) *have you change/have you changed* your musical style at all?

B: No, I (8) *haven't changed/hadn't changed* anything. My fans love me as I am.

2 Complete the dialogues. Use verbs from the box in the Present Perfect Simple negative.

> be   meet   play   taste   read   ~~watch~~

A: *Is this TV programme good?*

B: *I don't know I haven't watched it.*

1 A: Do you like Rome?
   B: I don't know. I _____ there.

2 A: Is the spaghetti ready?
   B: I don't know. I _____ it.

3 A: Do you like the new computer game?
   B: I don't know. I _____ it.

4 A: Do you like Gabriel's new book?
   B: I don't know. I _____ it.

5 A: What do you think of Sam's new boyfriend?
   B: I don't know. I _____ him.

3 Put the questions to these answers in the correct order.

1 A: countries to have you how many travelled?
   _____
   B: I've travelled to five different countries.

2 A: have eaten ever sushi you?
   _____
   B: No, I've never eaten sushi.

3 A: many how they worked countries have in?
   _____
   B: They've worked in three different countries.

4 A: have person you a famous ever met?
   _____
   B: I haven't met a famous person.

5 A: finished homework his has he?
   _____
   B: No, he hasn't finished his homework.

6 A: won how awards has many music she?
   _____
   B: She's won four different music awards.

7 A: seen film the have they?
   _____
   B: No, they haven't seen the film.

8 A: broken how records has he many world?
   _____
   B: He's broken three world records.

9 A: you ever have prize won a?
   _____
   B: Yes, I've won lots of prizes for my music.

10 A: played ever have you netball?
   _____
   B: I don't know what netball is! So no, I haven't.

4 Find the errors in six of these sentences and correct them.

1 Ive seen that film seven times!

2 She've been to France and Italy but she hasn't been to Greece.

3 Have you ever travelled by high speed train?

4 I haven't find the new museum.

5 They's broken five world records in the last two years.

6 No, she hasn't studied Korean before.

7 I haven't moved house in the last ten years.

8 I've eaten there last July.

9 I haven't tasted sashimi.

10 He's never meet my parents.

Pre-Int. Workbook Total English 2011
A. Clare, J.J. Wilson, W. Moreton

Vocabulary | achievements

5 Complete the text with the correct tense of the verbs from the box.

> do earn get give learn pass
> start win

Musicians Exchange

Address: http://www.musiciansexchange.com

I was born in Paraguay in 1980 and I started playing the violin when I was three years old. When I was twelve, I (1) _____ a prize for Young Musician of the Year. I came to England to study music. I also (2) _____ to speak English. I (3) _____ my music exams in 1997 and went to the US where I (4) _____ a good job with an orchestra. I didn't (5) _____ a lot of money with the orchestra but it was great experience. I wrote articles for the *New York Musician* magazine and (6) _____ speeches at many music colleges. In 2009, I (7) _____ my company, MusiciansExchange.com. The company organises international travel for music students and we also (8) _____ a lot of work for charity.

6 Which of the things from the text have or haven't you done? Write one sentence for each prompt:

win a prize   *I haven't won a prize.*

learn to speak English   *I have learned to speak English.*

1 pass an exam

   _____ .

2 get a good job

   _____ .

3 give speeches

   _____ .

4 start a company

   _____ .

5 do work for charity

   _____ .

Reading

7   **a** Read the text. Mark the sentences true (T) or false (F).

CHANNELS   MUSIC   SHOWS   NEWS   VIDE

MTV's VMAs
(Video Music Awards)

MTV's Video Music Awards are the most important prizes awarded for music videos. It all started in New York in 1984. The first band to win the Video of the Year award was the Cars for their video *You Might Think*. On the night of the awards famous singers and bands perform live. Bands which have performed at the awards include the Rolling Stones, Aerosmith, U2 and The Spice Girls. Lots of famous actors and musicians have presented the awards, including Eddie Murphy, Jack Black and Jamie Foxx. The awards show has taken place in various cities like New York, Los Angeles and London. The artist who has won the most VMAs? Madonna.

Some famous moments at the MTV awards:

In 1989 Paula Abdul won four awards. In 1992, the bass guitar player for Nirvana, Krist Novoselic threw his guitar in the air and it hit him on the head! In 1999, Britney Spears appeared on the show for the first time. In 2005, Spanish videos first competed in the awards.

1 The VMAs started in New York in 1986.

2 The Cars won the first Video of the Year award.

3 U2 haven't performed at the VMAs.

4 The VMAs have taken place in London.

5 Eddie Murphy and Jack Black have presented the awards.

6 Madonna has won the most VMAs.

7 A spectator hit Krist Novoselic on the head with a bottle at the awards.

8 Spanish videos competed for the first time in the awards in 2003.

b Correct the false sentences.

Vocabulary | word families

1 Complete the text with the correct form of the words in brackets.

Do you feel you don't have any (1) _____ (energetic)? Is stress a problem for you? Do the (2) _____ (intelligent) thing and take a break at Music Spa. It's the most (3) _____ (relaxing) spa in Europe!

Many of our customers are (4) _____ (tired) after working hard all year. They come to Music Spa for (5) _____ (relaxing). We offer massages and music therapy and if you prefer more (6) _____ (energetic) activities, we have a 40-metre swimming pool. Or you can use your (7) _____ (imaginative) and join our painting course.

Enjoy the relaxing atmosphere at Music Spa. You will leave the spa feeling full of (8) _____ (energetic)!

Visit www.musicspaprague.com for prices, availability and booking.

Pronunciation | stress patterns

2 a 🔊 6 What is the stress pattern of the words? Listen and write one word in each column.

energetic energy intelligent imagination
imaginative relaxing tiring

1	Oo	
2	Ooo	
3	oOo	
4	ooOo	
5	oOoo	
6	oOooo	
7	oooOo	

b Listen again and check your answers.

c 🔊 7 Listen and repeat the sentences.
1 He's really energetic.
2 I have no energy.
3 It's very relaxing.
4 She's really intelligent.
5 They have no imagination.
6 What an imaginative idea!
7 Running is tiring.

Grammar | questions

3 Write the questions for these answers.
1 A: _____ ?
   B: I work in the centre of town.
2 A: _____ ?
   B: I've been to France and Germany.
3 A: _____ ?
   B: I saw him at the café.
4 A: _____ ?
   B: My favourite music is hip hop.
5 A: _____ ?
   B: I go to the park at the weekends.
6 A: _____ ?
   B: I'm learning to play the piano at the moment.
7 A: _____ ?
   B: No, I don't play a musical instrument.
8 A: _____ ?
   B: I got up at about seven thirty on Monday.

4 Add one word to complete each question.

1 You ever been to France?
2 What sort of music you like listening to?
3 What music you listening to at the moment?
4 How many concerts you seen?
5 What the last CD you bought?
6 You see the match yesterday?
7 You going to English classes at the moment?
8 You got an MP3 player?

5 Here are some notes written by a journalist who is going to interview a rock star. Look at her notes and complete the questions.

biggest influences?
1 Who _____ ?
start singing?
2 When _____ ?
play concerts in the US?
3 Have you _____ ?
awards won?
4 How many _____ ?
meet any famous actors?
5 Have you _____ ?
like start acting?
6 Would you _____ ?

6 Match these answers to the questions in exercise 5.

a I've won three major awards.
b No. I'm not really interested in anything except music.
c When I was twelve. I started in the school choir!
d Probably Led Zeppelin. I used to listen to them a lot when I was young.
e No, I haven't.
f We've played three big concerts in New York. I want to go back there next year.

Listening

7 **a** 🔵 8 Cover the audioscript and listen to two people talking about their favourite music. Complete the table with (✓) if they like this type of music, and (✗) if they don't.

	Jazz	Rock	Dance	Classical
Pavel	✓			
Helena				

b Complete the audioscript with one word in each gap.

AUDIOSCRIPT

Pavel
Well, I'm (1) _____ jazz at the moment. I bought this CD about three months ago and I really love it. I don't know anything about jazz, but I'm learning! In the past I (2) _____ to a lot of rock music, which I still like. I love (3) _____ like the Rolling Stones and Led Zeppelin. And I like dance music too. In fact the only (4) _____ I don't listen to is classical. I just find it boring. My parents always listen to classical music but I just don't like it.

Helena
I grew up listening to classical music. Mainly Beethoven, Mozart and a lot of Italian opera, and this is what I love listening (5) _____ in the evening. Also I'm (6) _____ into jazz music, especially singers like Louis Armstrong and Nina Simone. I (7) _____ love to sing like them or play an instrument, the piano or the guitar. I can (8) _____ music, but I can't play anything. So, yes, I love music but not all types. I don't like rock or dance music very much.

Lifelong learning | recording vocabulary

8 **a** Look at the notes this students made about a word.

> boring
> (1) **bor**ing   (2) (adjective)
> (3) not interesting
> (4) Classical music is boring

b What information has the student written about the word? Write the number next to the type of information.

stress 1
example sentence ☐
definition ☐
part of speech ☐

3 Taste

Vocabulary | food, drink, people, kitchen equipment

1 Match the things in the pictures to the words below.

1	knife = ____	7	cooker = ____
2	fork = ____	8	chef = ____
3	spoon = ____	9	customer = ____
4	ice cream = ____	10	spaghetti = ____
5	mineral water = ____	11	meat = ____
6	saucepan = ____	12	vegetables = ____

2 Complete the sentences with the words from the box.

> allergic   chefs   diets   main   menu   recipe
> review   traditional   vegetarian

If you can't eat a type of food because you get ill you are *allergic* to that food.

1 The instructions for making a meal are called the _____ .

2 A typical type of food from a country is a _____ dish.

3 The biggest part of a meal is the _____ course.

4 The people who cook in restaurants are the _____ .

5 The list of what you can eat in a restaurant or café is the _____ .

6 _____ can help you to lose weight.

7 A report about a restaurant in a newspaper or magazine is a _____ .

8 A person who doesn't eat meat or fish is a _____ .

3 The words in **bold** are in the wrong sentences. Put them in the correct sentences.

1 I've bought a new **customers** for the kitchen. It cooks food really quickly.

2 The **cooker** was really angry with his boss.

3 That café is really busy – it's always full of **plums**.

4 I don't eat fruit very often but I love **waitress**.

5 That **bread** is very unfriendly. She never smiles.

6 I like sandwiches made with brown **waiter**.

Listening

4 **a** 💿 9 Cover the audioscript. Listen to the programme about Delia Smith and answer the questions.

1 What jobs did Delia have before she started cooking?

2 How old was Delia when she started working in a restaurant in London?

3 In what year did she start to write in the *Daily Mirror* magazine?

4 When did she start presenting the television show *Family Fare*?

5 What type of books does she write?

6 What happens when Delia recommends ingredients?

b Listen again and check your answers.

AUDIOSCRIPT

Delia Smith is a famous British TV chef who appears on TV programmes. Before she was a chef she worked as a hairdresser and in a travel agency. When she was twenty-one, she started work in a small restaurant in London. In 1969 Delia Smith started to write for the *Daily Mirror* magazine. She also wrote in the newspaper *The Evening Standard*. Her first television show was *Family Fare* which she presented from 1973 to 1975 and another television series, *Delia's How to Cook* was a big success. She writes cookery books too. When Delia recommends ingredients on her programmes or in her books, these ingredients often sell more in supermarkets. Some people call this the 'Delia Effect'.

Reading

5 Choose the correct words to complete the text.

	A	B	C	D
1	top-lesson	top-class	topping	top page
2	passion	passionate	passionately	passions
3	success	exciting	successful	excite
4	afford	affording	can't afford	affordable
5	experiences	experienced	experiencing	experience
6	habit	habitual	customs	habits

FINEDINING.CO.UK

TUBE Covent Garden
CUISINE Italian
AVERAGE PRICE £35 (45 euro)
Neal St Restaurant

Antonio Carluccio, a (1) _____ Italian chef opened this restaurant over twenty-two years ago. He has a (2) _____ for great food, and the menu has some very tasty recipes, for example pasta dishes with mushrooms and grilled fish. The restaurant is in Covent Garden and has become a real (3) _____ story. This is probably because although the food is great it is still a very (4) _____ restaurant. Antonio has plans to open six new restaurants in London. This will mean 250 new staff but all the waiters and waitresses need to have previous restaurant (5) _____ and speak Italian. I love this restaurant and my own cooking (6) _____ have changed – I now often cook pasta at home – although it is never as good as Antonio's!

Grammar | *be going to*: future plans

6 Look at the pictures and complete the sentences using *going to* and the verb in brackets.

He isn't going to buy a new car. (buy)

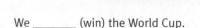

1 We _____ (win) the World Cup.

2 They _____ on the beach. (play)

3 I _____ . (be)

4 He _____ . (pass)

5 They _____ . (get married)

7 Find and correct the mistakes in these sentences.

1 Pete and Kate is going to stay in a hotel this weekend.

2 They not going to finish the work before next week.

3 I'm not going to is at the party next week.

4 He are going to visit the Opera House in Sydney in the summer.

5 I'm not going study French next year.

6 There going to do a computer course next week.

7 Are you going play football this weekend?

8 You going to eat at that new restaurant this weekend?

Pronunciation |
connected speech (1)

8 **a** ⊕ 10 Listen and mark the links between consonants and vowels in these sentences.

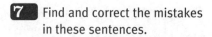

1 She's going to a party on Saturday night at the nightclub.

2 I'm going to have lunch on Friday at a really good restaurant.

3 I'm going to have fish and chips from a café.

4 The college trains chefs in restaurants.

5 They're going to walk around the town on Monday.

6 Did you hear about the new restaurant on Main Street?

7 They're teaching the children about food and drink.

b Listen again and check your answers.

3.2

New Total English
Pre-Int. Workbook
Pearson Longman 2011

Vocabulary | describing food

1 Complete the sentences with the adjectives from the box.

> ~~baked~~   boiled   fresh   fried   grilled   raw
> savoury   spicy   sweet

I love hot baked bread – it's delicious!

1 I eat a lot of chocolate and other _____ food.
2 I hate hot, _____ foods like curry.
3 She's very healthy – she eats lots of _____ fruit and vegetables.
4 I love eating _____ barbecue food.
5 A lot of Americans like big breakfasts with _____ bacon and eggs.
6 I like _____ snacks – I don't like food with a lot of sugar.
7 Has the water for the tea _____ yet?
8 _____ vegetables are vegetables which aren't cooked at all.

2 Complete the email with the correct words.

Hi from Peru!

We're having a great time here. We met up with my old secretary, Paola, and she's been showing us around Lima. I know you love food, so I'm going to tell you all about what we have been eating!

The first night we arrived we went to a restaurant near Paola's house and we had something very typical: *ceviche*. This is (1) _____ fish, yes that's right – not cooked at all! It has lots of lemon on it and it is very tasty. We also had *papa rellena* which is potato filled with meat and eggs and (2) _____ in hot oil. We had some great (3) _____ salad too. We then had a lovely dessert called *alfajores*. They seemed to have a lot of sugar and were very (4) _____.

Yesterday Paola took us outside Lima to a fiesta. We had a lot of meat! Paola told me it was called *pachamanca*. The meat is (5) _____ like bread in an underground oven. We also had something called *rocoto relleno* which was really hot and (6) _____. We also had something called *ocopa*. This is a sauce made with yellow potatoes (7) _____ in water. Paola has invited us to her cousin's barbecue tomorrow. She has promised us a lot of (8) _____ meat. She says it's going to be really tasty!

1	**A** raw	**B** cooked	**C** cold	**D** hot
2	**A** roast	**B** grilled	**C** fried	**D** baked
3	**A** fresh	**B** boiled	**C** roast	**D** sweet
4	**A** savoury	**B** raw	**C** sweet	**D** roast
5	**A** boiled	**B** spicy	**C** grilled	**D** baked
6	**A** spicy	**B** sweet	**C** savoury	**D** fresh
7	**A** fried	**B** boiled	**C** roast	**D** baked
8	**A** boiled	**B** sweet	**C** grilled	**D** raw

Grammar | Present Continuous: future arrangements

3 Complete the sentences with the Present Continuous and the words in brackets. Use contracted forms where possible.

1 **A:** What _____ (you/do) this evening?
   B: I _____ (stay) at home and _____ (watch) television.
2 **A:** _____ (you/cook) supper later?
   B: No. We _____ (have) a takeaway pizza.
3 **A:** _____ (you/do) anything this afternoon?
   B: I don't know. I _____ (not play) tennis with Liam because _____ (rain).
4 **A:** How _____ (you/get) home from the meeting?
   B: I _____ (not drive). I _____ (take) the six o'clock train.
5 **A:** _____ (you/come) to the football match on Saturday?
   B: Yes. We _____ (bring) a friend too.
6 **A:** We _____ (not go) on holiday next week.
   B: Matt _____ (go) to hospital.
7 **A:** Help! I'm not ready.
   B: Don't worry. The guests _____ (not arrive) until 8:30.
8 **A:** _____ (you/come) to the office on Monday?
   B: No. I _____ (not work) next week.

4 Complete the sentences with verbs from the box in the Present Continuous.

> finish   go   have   leave   meet
> move   play   take   work   visit

1 We _____ sailing this weekend on Charlotte's new boat.
2 They _____ for France on Friday morning.
3 I _____ the Natural History Museum this afternoon.
4 He _____ the bank manager tomorrow morning.
5 _____ you _____ football on Saturday?
6 We _____ not _____ house this month.
7 Rachel _____ a baby soon.
8 _____ they _____ a train to Venice?
9 We _____ on this project for two weeks.
10 He _____ the painting tomorrow.

18

5 Write the questions for these answers.

1 A: _____ ?
   B: No, I'm not going to the party.
2 A: _____ ?
   B: At two o'clock I'm playing football.
3 A: _____ ?
   B: We're meeting Zara in the pub.
4 A: _____ ?
   B: Yes, I'm staying at the hotel.
5 A: _____ ?
   B: I'm studying because I've got an exam on Friday.
6 A: _____ ?
   B: I'm travelling to Dublin by car.
7 A: _____ ?
   B: I'm buying Oliver a new shirt for his birthday.
8 A: _____ ?
   B: I'm staying in Tokyo for a week.

How to... | make arrangements

6 **a** 🔵 11 Listen to Jim inviting two women out. Write notes in the table.

Sal	
Plans:	*staying at home*
Reason:	

Bella	
Plans (Sat):	
Reason:	
Plans (Sun):	

b Write sentences to say what the women are doing at the weekend.

1 Sal is staying home to study for her exams.
2 On Saturday, Bella _____ .
3 On Sunday, Bella _____ .

7 Number the lines of the dialogues in the correct order. Listen again to check.

Dialogue 1

☐ Hello Jim.
☐ Thanks Jim. I'll tell you ...
☐ Not really. I'm staying at home to study for my exams.
1 Hello, Sal. It's Jim.
☐ OK. I'll call you again next week. Good luck with your exams!
☐ Oh, that's really nice of you but I don't like going out when I have to study. I'm sorry. Perhaps another time?
☐ Are you doing anything this weekend?
☐ I see. Well why don't you come out for a drink on Saturday evening? There's a new bar opening on the river ...

Dialogue 2

☐ What are you doing on Saturday evening?
☐ Hello, Bella? It's Jim.
☐ Perfect! I can meet you on the river at 7:00 p.m.
☐ Nothing. Why?
☐ 7:30 would be better for me. I'm going to Oxford on Sunday to visit my aunt and I'm driving so I won't be back ...
☐ Well, would you like to come out for a drink, or something to eat?
☐ Hello.
☐ Great idea! Oh, wait a minute. Saturday? No, I've just remembered. I'm going to a concert on Saturday. Diane's bought some tickets to see Coldplay. Why don't we go out on Sunday evening?

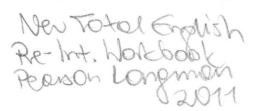
New Total English
Re-Int. Workbook
Pearson Longman
2011

Grammar | defining relative clauses

1 **a** Complete the crossword clues with *who, which* or *where*.

Down

1 It's the person _____ serves your food.
2 It's something _____ is very cold and you can eat it at the end of a meal.
3 It's someone _____ eats in a restaurant.
4 They are the instructions _____ you use for cooking a particular dish.
7 They are the things _____ you use for cutting.
8 It's the meal _____ you eat in the middle of the day.

Across

5 It's the dish _____ you eat before your main course.
6 It's a place _____ you can buy fresh fruit and vegetables.
9 It's the room _____ a chef works.
10 It's the person _____ cooks your meal.

b Use the clues to complete the crossword.

2 Complete the sentences with *who, which* or *where*.

1 A builder is someone _____ builds houses.
2 A cooker is a machine _____ cooks food.
3 An airport is a place _____ people catch planes.
4 A pilot is someone _____ flies planes.
5 A pencil is something _____ you use for writing or drawing.
6 An author is someone _____ writes books.
7 A cinema is a place _____ you go to watch movies.

3 Write a definition for the words below. Include defining relative clauses in your definitions.

magazine

1 cinema   5 recipe
2 lead singer   6 chef
3 soundtrack   7 theatre
4 cooker   8 restaurant

A *magazine* is something which you read.

1 _____
2 _____
3 _____
4 _____
5 _____
6 _____
7 _____
8 _____

Vocabulary | easily-confused words

4 Choose the correct alternative.

1 Did you get a *recipe/receipt* for the present you bought her in case she wants to change it?
2 That *chef/chief* is really famous – he cooks in a really good restaurant.
3 The waiters were really *educated/polite* and nice in that restaurant.
4 He always eats really *sensible/sensitive* food, lots of fruit and vegetables.
5 I thought the Indian restaurant was on the corner but *actually/now* it was across the street.
6 We bought a new *cook/cooker* for the kitchen.
7 They had a terrible *discussion/argument* at dinner – they were shouting at each other.

Reading

5 **a** Read the text and choose the best title.

- The Most Expensive Pizza in the World
- The Most Expensive Fast Food in the World.
- Very Expensive Food.

Fast food is normally fast and cheap. People don't want to pay a lot of money for a hamburger and fries or for a pizza, but there are some exceptions. Here is some of the world's most expensive fast food.

A restaurant in Glasgow, Scotland has a very expensive pizza. How much does it cost? More than two thousand dollars! What does this pizza have that other pizzas don't have? Well, the ingredients are very expensive and include small pieces of gold!

A lot of people prefer burgers to pizzas. So where can you buy a really expensive burger? Well, perhaps the world's most expensive burger can be eaten in Las Vegas. A restaurant there is selling a burger for five thousand dollars! It is made of the best Japanese meat.

And what about an expensive hot dog? Well, Germany is the home of the sausage so it is a good place to buy a hot dog. In a hotel in Berlin you can buy maybe the most expensive hot dog in the world. It costs two hundred euros.

And after the burger or pizza if you want to have ice cream you can go to a famous restaurant in New York and pay one thousand dollars for an ice cream. For this money you get a wonderful ice cream which comes with a gold spoon. You can take the spoon home after you finish eating!

b Read the text again and answer the questions.

1 How much does the pizza in the restaurant in Glasgow cost?
2 Where can you buy a very expensive burger?
3 Where does the meat in the expensive burger come from?
4 How much does the hot dog in Berlin cost?
5 Where can you pay one thousand dollars for an ice cream?
6 What can you take home after eating the ice cream?

Pronunciation | silent letters

6 **a** 🔊 12 Listen and underline the words in each sentence with silent letters.

1 My daughter hurt her knee.
2 The writer thought about her book.
3 It was a cold night in Autumn.
4 There were eight foreigners.
5 Could you take the dog for a walk?
6 I know you're wrong.
7 The sign was high in the sky.

b Write the underlined words in the table.

Silent g	Silent w	Silent l	Silent k	Silent n
daughter				

Lifelong learning | defining what you mean

7 Put the words in the correct order to make sentences.

1 use It's bottles. for opening which you something
2 yourself. that thing you It's to the dry use
3 stuff bread. can put It's you the on which
4 changing the for which thing the TV. you use It's programme
5 can It's cook that you in. something
6 your the put It's food. that stuff you white on

Present Simple vs Present Continuous

1 <u>Underline</u> the correct verb form.

1 *Are you leaving/Do you leave* now?

2 Sam *doesn't usually wear/isn't usually wearing* jeans.

3 I *am never watching/never watch* TV.

4 Who *does James talk/is James talking* to?

5 *Do you know/Are you knowing* my wife, Samira?

6 She *is sometimes going/sometimes goes* out.

7 **A:** Can I help you?
   B: I *look/am looking* for this dress, in size 12.

8 The manager *often has lunch/is often having lunch* in his office.

9 **A:** What *are you doing/do you do*?
   B: I'm waiting for the train.

10 It *doesn't rain/isn't raining* now.

2 Write the questions. Match them to the answers a–j.

1 What/you/do?
   _____ ?

2 Where/you/go?
   _____ ?

3 What/she/eat?
   _____ ?

4 Where/they/live?
   _____ ?

5 What time/you/get home?
   _____ ?

6 You/go/the shops?
   _____ ?

7 What/Paul/do?
   _____ ?

8 You/enjoy/your course?
   _____ ?

9 How/get/to work?
   _____ ?

10 Jayne/have/a car?
   _____ ?

a Yes. Do you want me to buy something?

b No, she doesn't.

c In South Africa.

d I walk.

e To the dentist. I've got an appointment.

f I'm a teacher.

g Usually at about 7 p.m.

h Yes. I'm learning a lot.

i He's playing tennis.

j Vegetable soup with pasta.

Past Simple vs Present Perfect

3 <u>Underline</u> the correct verb form.

The Goddesses

The Goddesses are a new girl band from Dublin. They (1) *started/have started* playing in 2002, and (2) *have made/made* fourteen albums. Their first album (3) *sold/has sold* 50,000 copies in the first two months. They (4) *have won/won* the Irish Music Awards twice, and (5) *have toured/toured* around Europe and America. Why (6) *have they been/were they* so successful?

Amy and Sam, the lead singers, are sisters. 'We (7) *have always loved/always loved* singing. When we were at primary school we (8) *started/have started* a band with some friends and (9) *sang/have sung* in a concert at the end of the year. It (10) *was/has been* a great success. Since that day we (11) *have always been/were always* very lucky.'

4 Complete the text with the correct form of the verbs in brackets.

I (1) _____ (live) in London for three years now. I (2) _____ (come) here at first to learn English as I needed to get a better job back in Poland. I (3) _____ (be) to loads of different cities but London is my favourite. The first time I (4) _____ (see) the centre of London I fell in love with it. When I (5) _____ (arrive) I started studying in a language school. I also (6) _____ (start) work in a café in the kitchen. I (7) _____ (have) a few other jobs since then, always in cafés or restaurants. I (8) _____ (travel) all over England but I (9) _____ (not find) a city that I like more than London.

going to and Present Continuous (for future plans/arrangements)

5 Write the questions for these answers.

1 A: _____
   B: No, I'm not meeting her this afternoon.

2 A: _____
   B: I'm seeing Tariq this weekend.

3 A: _____
   B: Yes, she's playing badminton on Saturday.

4 A: _____
   B: We are eating at the local café.

5 A: _____
   B: We're going on holiday to Paris.

6 A: _____
   B: I'm flying to Hong Kong.

7 A: _____
   B: He is going to buy a new computer.

8 A: _____
   B: No, we aren't going to take the train.

Defining relative clauses

6 Complete the sentences using *which*, *who* or *where*.

1 It's the place _____ I normally meet her.
2 He's the man _____ I met last night.
3 It's something _____ you use if you want to play tennis.
4 This is the school _____ I started playing football.
5 The thing _____ I find the easiest is the accounting.
6 That's the book _____ Simpson wrote.
7 There's the beach _____ we went last summer.
8 She's the teacher _____ I was most frightened of.

7 Put the relative clauses (a–f) in the correct place in the sentences (1–6).

a who has his own software company
b which you can't find
c which has double rooms for 50 euros
d where we had our first meal together
e who offered me her seat on the bus
f ~~which you gave me~~

I can't find that bag.

I can't find that bag which you gave me.

1 Are these the keys?

   _____

2 Do you remember the restaurant?

   _____

3 Do you know the name of that hotel?

   _____

4 That's the woman.

   _____

5 My sister introduced me to a man.

   _____

Vocabulary

8 Put these words in the correct column to form phrases.

> a lie-in   a lot of work for charity   a nap
> a prize   a take-away   an award   bowling
> clubbing   for a walk   ice skating
> nothing   shopping   some exercise

do	go	have	win

9 Complete the sentences using the words from the box.

> check   cooker   download   earns
> energetic   flop   spicy   time   stressful
> vegetarian

1 'Do you eat meat or fish?' 'No, I'm a _____ .'
2 I always _____ my emails as soon as I get to work.
3 She bought a new electric _____ for her kitchen because the old one was broken.
4 It is illegal to _____ songs from the Internet without paying.
5 That film was a complete _____ – nobody went to see it.
6 He is doing two jobs at the same _____ . I don't how he does it.
7 She _____ a lot of money in her new job.
8 She's really _____ . She does lots of sports and is always running around.

10 Put the underlined verbs in the correct sentences.

1 He passed his own company last year and is making a lot of money.
2 'What are you doing for lunch?' 'I'm take a meal with my family.'
3 I'm talking to speak Russian at the moment. It's really difficult.
4 'What are you doing?' 'I'm learning on the phone to Sophie.'
5 He's having a lot of problems at school – he hasn't started an exam yet.
6 I normally have to having the train at 7:20 to get to work on time.

Vocabulary | collocations

1 Complete the sentences with the correct words from the box.

> abroad   control   extreme   goal   interview   raise   rely   strength

1 I had a job _____ the other day – I didn't get the job though.
2 I want to travel _____ this summer, maybe to France.
3 He loves _____ sports like mountain climbing and free-diving.
4 They ran a marathon to _____ money for charity.
5 She achieved her _____ of climbing Mont Blanc.
6 I find it difficult to _____ my fear of flying – I hate planes.
7 When climbing in the Himalayas you have to _____ on a team to help you.
8 He has a lot of physical _____ – he goes to the gym four times a week.

Grammar | comparative adjectives

2 Read the texts below and complete the sentences using the words in brackets.

ABT EXTREME SPORTS HOLIDAYS

Kayaking, mountain climbing, base jumping and free diving.

ACCOMMODATION:
4-star hotel, all meals provided.

YOU NEED TO BE:
over 16, a strong swimmer, very fit.

COST:
One week: $500   One month: $1,500

Knockout Vacations

Try 15 extreme sports! Minimum age is 18.
No experience necessary. Beginners welcome.
Non-stop fun and games!

Accommodation: simple flats for 6 people.
Price: $349 per person. All vacations last 7 days.

For a knockout holiday you will never forget!

1 These course at ABT are _____ _____ _____ (expensive) the courses at Knockout.
2 ABT has _____ (good) accommodation _____ Knockout.
3 Knockout sounds _____ _____ _____ (enjoyable) ABT.
4 Knockout seems _____ _____ (friendly) ABT.
5 You can do _____ (long) courses at ABT.
6 Knockout has a _____ (great) variety _____ ABT.
7 ABT welcomes people who are _____ _____ (young) eighteen.
8 For ABT you need to be _____ _____ (fit) normal people.

3 Rewrite the second sentences so that they mean the same as the first sentences. Use the adjectives in brackets. Change the form if necessary.

1 The Atlantic is 76.762 million square km. The Pacific is 155.557 million square km.
(big)
The Pacific _____ the Atlantic.
2 Free diving is dangerous. Swimming isn't dangerous.
(dangerous)
Free diving is _____ swimming.
3 Mountain climbing is difficult. Without oxygen it is very difficult.
(difficult)
Mountain climbing with oxygen isn't _____ mountain climbing without oxygen.
4 Physical strength is important for divers. Mental strength is very important.
(important)
Physical strength _____ as mental strength, for divers.
5 Temba Tsheri climbed Everest when he was 15. Sherman Bull May climbed Everest when he was 64.
(old)
Temba Tsheri wasn't as _____ Sherman Bull May when he climbed Everest.
6 Junichi Koide dived 132 metres. Tanya Streeter dived 160 metres.
(deep)
Tanya dived _____ Junichi.

4 **a** Read the text about the brothers and mark the sentences true (T) or false (F).

> I have three brothers, Martin, Tim and James. Martin is 1m 96 tall, Tim is 1m 94 and James is 1m 78. Tim is very intelligent – he got five As in his last exams. Martin got four As. James didn't get any As. James is really fit. He can run without stopping for ten kilometres. Martin and Tim can't run for more than two minutes! Martin is very talented. He paints really well and also plays three musical instuments. James plays the guitar well but Tim isn't talented at all!

Martin   Tim   James

1 Martin is much taller than Tim.
2 Tim is a bit shorter than Martin.
3 Tim is a bit more intelligent than James.
4 James is much fitter than Martin.
5 James is a bit fitter than Tim.
6 Martin is much more talented than Tim.

b Correct the false sentences.

Reading

5 Read the text and mark the sentences true (T) or false (F).

> You've heard of a normal marathon? More than 42 kilometres running through a city. Difficult? Well, here's a more difficult race. The Kalahari Extreme Marathon is a marathon which is seven days long. The total distance of the marathon is about 250 km. But it's not just a long race, it's also a hot one. The marathon is in the Kalahari Desert in Africa. During the race temperatures can be very hot – in the day temperatures can be more than 40°C. At night it gets very cold, sometimes less than than 5°C.
>
> The race is normally around 250 km long but the actual distance changes every year – sometimes it can be longer. To make it more difficult for the runners, they only know the exact distance and where they are going to run the day before they start running. To do this marathon, runners need to be very fit. They also need to drink lots of water! Is this the most difficult marathon in the world?

1 A normal marathon is longer than the Kalahari Extreme marathon.
2 The Kalahari Extreme marathon is more than 42 kilometres long.
3 You need seven days to run the Kalahari marathon.
4 Sometimes it is hotter than 40°C during the race.
5 Temperatures at night in the Kalahari are always more than 5°C.
6 The runners know where they are going to run the week before the marathon.
7 It is important for runners to drink a lot of water during the race.

Vocabulary | describing people

6 Complete the sentences with adjectives which describe people.

1 She gives lots of presents to her friends. She's really g_____ .
2 No one can stop him when he wants something. He's really d_____ .
3 She solves problems and understands things easily. She's i_____ .
4 She is sure that she is good enough. She's very c_____ .
5 He wants to be manager of this company by the time he's thirty. He's m_____ .
6 He can run for miles without getting tired. He's very f_____ .
7 She makes people laugh all the time. She's f_____ .
8 They always do what you ask them to do. They're really r_____ .
9 She is an incredible singer, dancer and actor. She's t_____ .
10 He has a very dangerous job. He's b_____ .

Pronunciation | emphasising important words

7 **a** 🔊 13 Listen and underline the words in these sentences which have the weak forms /ðən/ and /əz/.

1 He's as strong as James.
2 She's a lot taller than Sheila.
3 Madrid's a smaller city than London.
4 Rugby's a more dangerous sport than football.
5 That book is not as interesting as the last one I read.
6 It's as big as this house.
7 The water's a bit deeper in this pool than in the small one.
8 This question is not as difficult as other ones.

b Listen again and practise saying the sentences.

Vocabulary | survival skills

1 Complete the sentences with words from the box.

> challenge   cope   myself   shelter   survival   wilderness

1 I can _____ with most problems at work.
2 I think maths is really difficult - for me it's a _____ .
3 I pushed _____ and in the end I finished the marathon.
4 He was lost in the desert but lived because of his _____ skills.
5 I would love to go on holiday to the _____ where there is no one at all.
6 If I was in the country in the rain I think I could build myself a _____ .

Grammar | superlative adjectives

2 Choose the correct words to complete the dialogue.

A: Hi, Steven. How are you?
B: Good. I've just been to the cinema to see the (1) *latest/later* Harry Potter.
A: Really? Where did you see it?
B: In the Stella Cinema. It's the (2) *baddest/worst* cinema I know. Well at least the (3) *most old/oldest*.
A: But if you go at lunchtime it's also the (4) *cheapest/most* cheap.
B: Yes, really cheap but it's also the (5) *farthest/furthest* from the centre.
A: What was the film like?
B: I think it's definitely the (6) *goodest/best* Harry Potter film. The action was great. It's also the (7) *frighteningest/most frightening* Potter and I think it will be the (8) *more popular/most popular*.
A: What about the acting?
B: They're not the (9) *talentedest/most talented* actors, but you don't notice because the film is so good.
A: Sounds good.

3 Read the text and make superlatives from the words in brackets.

SURVIVOR!

It's Big Brother, but on an island! Who will survive this time? Here are the four remaining contestants.

Mike is physically (1) ____ (strong) contestant. He loves nature and he likes to push himself to the limit. He isn't (2) ____ (intelligent) contestant.

Clara is from Ancona, Italy. She loves water and she is (3) ____ (good) swimmer in the group. She is (4) ____ (small) contestant but she has many survival skills.

Yevgeny likes challenges. He was in the Russian army for five years. He says it was (5) ____ (hard) time of his life but he enjoyed it. Yevgeny is (6) ____ (popular) contestant because he has a good sense of humour.

Virginia is (7) ____ (tall) contestant. She played basketball for the US women's team. Now she works in a survival school. She is (8) ____ (fit) person in the group.

4 Write sentences with the same meaning. Use the words in brackets. Write 2–5 words.

1 No runner is faster than Lewis.
Lewis _____ runner in the world. (the)

2 I have never eaten better food!
This is the _____ eaten. (ever)

3 There were not many easier exams.
This was one _____ exams. (of)

4 No other country in Europe has more tourists than Italy.
Italy is _____ tourist destination in Europe. (popular)

5 I've never stayed in a house this beautiful.
This is the _____ ever stayed in. (have)

6 The other theatres in the town are bigger than this one.
This is _____ the town. (theatre)

7 He is 100 kg. The other boys are not so heavy.
He _____ boy in the group. (is)

8 None of the other songs on the CD are as good as this one.
This is _____ song on the CD. (the)

9 I have never been to a nicer hotel.
This is _____ hotel I've ever been to. (the)

10 Her clothes are more expensive than anyone I know.
Her clothes are _____ of all my friends. (expensive)

Reading

5 Read the interview and mark the sentences true (T) or false (F).

The Most ...

This week in our series *The Most* ... we interview Will Sánchez, the star of *Wild Survival!* He's the man who goes to some of the most dangerous countryside in the world and has to survive in very difficult situations followed by a cameraman. Today he tells us about some of the extreme experiences he has survived in.

What's the most dangerous situation you've ever been in?

The most difficult situation has to be when I was filming in Colombia in the forest. I was climbing up a tree when the rope I was using to help me climb broke. I fell about ten metres before I hit a branch.

What is the most challenging countryside you have experienced?

The most challenging countryside was when I was in the Arctic Circle. Actually it's not really countryside at all. It's just snow and ice. And it's very, very cold.

What has been the most difficult thing you have had to do?

The most difficult thing I had to do was make a fire in the Arctic Circle. As I said it's very cold. But there is another problem: there isn't anything to make a fire with. In the end I did make the fire but it took a long time.

What is the most difficult situation to film in?

This is always when I am in water. It's very difficult for my cameraman, Scott to follow me in the water and to stay near me so that he can film what I am doing. And unfortunately, I'm jumping into water all the time!

1 Will Sanchéz is a cameraman.
2 When Will was climbing in Colombia, the tree broke.
3 Making a fire in the Arctic Circle is difficult because there is not a lot of material to make a fire with.
4 It's always easy for Scott to follow Will with the camera.
5 Will is often in water in the programme.

Lifelong learning | British and American English

1 **a** <u>Underline</u> the examples of American English vocabulary in the text.

I was standing in line in a fast food restaurant but I needed to go to the restroom. When I got back the line was really long so I had to wait for a long time. I started to think about what I was going to order: maybe a large hamburger with French fries and a big soda. I thought perhaps a cookie too. While I was in line my cell phone rang. It was my mum who was on vacation and had a problem. She was standing on the sidewalk because the car she was driving ran out of gas and she didn't know what to do. When I finished talking to her I finally got to the end of the line and I ordered my food. When the food came and I looked at the check I suddenly realised that I had left my purse in my apartment and I couldn't pay for all the food. I found two dollars in the pocket of my pants and I got a bag of chips instead.

b Change the American English words for British English words.

Grammar | indirect questions

2 Put the words in the correct order to complete the indirect questions.

1. what is the time
   Can you tell me _____ ?
2. can an Internet café find where I
   Do you know _____ ?
3. the tube is nearest where station
   Could you tell me _____ ?
4. what leaves the time next train
   Can you tell me _____ ?
5. Sunday on is the if museum open
   Do you know _____ ?
6. a costs ticket how much
   Can you tell me _____ ?
7. to airport how is far it the
   Could you tell me _____ ?
8. phonecard I where can buy a
   Can you tell me _____ ?

3 Change the questions below to indirect questions.

1. Where is the coffee shop?
   _____
2. What is the time?
   _____
3. Where can I pay for the theatre?
   _____
4. What time does the underground open?
   _____
5. Where is the bus station?
   _____
6. Where can I buy a ticket for the football match?
   _____

Listening

4 **a** 🔘 14 Listen to the dialogues. Where are the speakers? Choose a place from the map.

Dialogue 1 = *Camden Market*

Dialogue 2 = _____

Dialogue 3 = _____

Dialogue 4 = _____

Dialogue 5 = _____

Dialogue 6 = _____

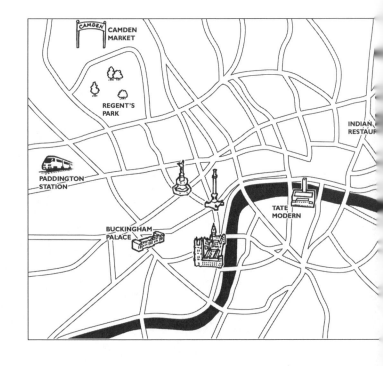

b Complete the dialogues. Write one word in each gap.

1 A: Can you tell me what time it (1) _____ ?
   B: What, the market?
   A: Yes.
   B: (2) _____ 6:00.
   A: 6.00. Thanks.

2 A: Excuse me. Can you tell me (3) _____ we can go inside the palace?
   B: Yes, you can. It costs £12 a ticket.
   A: OK, can we have two tickets, please?
   B: Certainly. That's £24. Thank you. (4) _____ the palace.

3 A: Do you know (5) _____ we can take photos of the paintings?
   B: Here in the gallery?
   A: Yes.
   B: No, you can't. There's a (6) _____ that says 'no photography'.
   A: Oh yes.

4 A: Excuse me, do you know where the (7) _____ tube station is?
   B: Yeah, go out of the park.
   A: Yes.
   B: Through the gardens. And it's (8) _____ five minutes' walk.
   A: Out of the park and about five minutes.
   B: That's right.
   A: Thanks.

5 A: Can you tell me (9) _____ a 'chicken phal' is?
   B: It's a chicken dish. Very, very hot.
   A: Oh really?
   B: Very spicy. But delicious.
   A: OK, I'll (10) _____ it.
   B: One chicken phal. Anything to drink?

6 A: Excuse me, do you know when the next train (11) _____ for Heathrow?
   B: Yes, you want the Heathrow Express. They leave every thirty minutes.
   A: Which platform?
   B: I don't know. You can ask (12) _____ there.
   A: Thank you very much.

c Listen and check your answers.

Reading

5 Read the text about Ireland and answer the questions.

1 What is the first official language in Ireland?
2 How many parts is Ireland divided into?
3 Why is Ireland called the Emerald Isle?
4 When did Seamus Heaney win the Nobel Prize for literature?
5 Can you touch the ball with your hands when playing Gaelic football?
6 What is a sliotar?

Ireland is one of many countries where English is spoken, although the first official language of Ireland is Irish. The island of Ireland is divided into two parts: The Republic of Ireland and Northern Ireland which is part of the United Kingdom. Ireland is known as the Emerald Isle because the countryside is very green. It rains a lot in Ireland!

Irish culture

Irish music is famous all over the world. Perhaps the most important Irish groups are U2 and the Cranberries. Ireland also has a strong tradition of writing. Famous Irish writers include Samuel Beckett, W.B. Yeats, George Bernard Shaw and Oscar Wilde. All of these writers won the Nobel Prize for literature. Poet Seamus Heaney was the last Irishman to win the Nobel Prize for literature, in 1995.

Irish sports

The Irish love sports, including football, rugby and horse racing. There are two other traditional Irish sports which are very popular: Gaelic football and hurling. Gaelic football is played with a round ball like a football. In Gaelic football you can kick the ball but you can also catch it in your hands. In hurling the players play with sticks and a small hard ball called a sliotar. Both of these sports are very fast.

Vocabulary | stages

1 Put these words in order, 1 being the youngest stage of life, 10 the oldest.

adolescent ☐
adult ☐
baby ☐
child ☐
middle-aged man/woman ☐
old/elderly ☐
retired man/woman ☐
toddler ☐
young adult ☐

2 Complete the crossword clues with one word. Write the words in the crossword.

Across

3 Doctors and lawyers earn a good _____ in my country. (Mohamed, Egypt)

5 You can learn to _____ a car when you are seventeen. (Mick, the UK)

7 Women usually _____ married in their late thirties. (Inge, Norway)

8 Most women _____ children in their twenties. (Nobantu, Malawi)

9 Most people _____ when they are sixty-five. (Gavin, Scotland)

Down

1 It's expensive to get a _____ of your own. (Ale, Spain)

2 We _____ from university in our twenties. (Laura, Ireland)

4 Grandparents often _____ after the kids. (Romina, Italy)

Grammar | *should, have to, can*: obligation and permission

3 **a** Read what four people say about their jobs. Complete the sentences using the words in brackets.

Diane

(*don't have to/can't/have to*)

1 Most people ____ afford my designs.

2 I ____ attend all the fashion shows, but I do because I enjoy them.

3 I ____ work hard before Fashion Week in October. There are many things to do.

Karl

(*don't have to/shouldn't/can*)

4 We ____ eat chocolate or sweets, but sometimes we do.

5 We ____ go to the gym but we go sometimes.

6 You ____ earn a lot of money if you play for the national team.

Rafael

(*can't/have to/should*)

7 I ____ take long holidays because the company needs me in the office.

8 I ____ speak to all my workers but I don't always have time.

9 I ____ make important business decisions.

Siegfried

(*have to/shouldn't/should*)

10 I tell people that they ____ eat too much sugar.

11 I tell people that they ____ visit me three times a year.

12 I ____ look into people's mouths every day.

b What jobs do they do? Choose from the words in the box.

actress   businessman
dentist   doctor
fashion designer   footballer
gardener   journalist
lawyer   singer   taxi driver
teacher

4 Read the story and choose the correct alternative.

A day in the life of a Spanish primary school pupil – aged eight.

I get up at seven thirty when my dad calls me. I always try to stay in bed for another few minutes so my dad (1) *has to/should* come back and get me out of bed. I have cereal and a glass of milk for breakfast. I then put my uniform on. I (2) *have to/can't* wear a uniform or the school tracksuit every day.

We (3) *don't have to/can* get the metro or the bus to school but we normally take the bus because the bus stop is near my house. I start school at nine o'clock. I have a break at eleven o'clock when I have a sandwich and a drink. I (4) *can't/should* eat sweets at breaktime. I go back to class until one thirty when I have lunch. After lunch I have more classes until five o'clock. When the classes finish I play football or basketball until six. My mum collects me and we go home.

When I get home I (5) *have to/shouldn't* do a lot of homework. I (6) *can't/can* watch a lot of TV because my parents don't let me, but I watch about half an hour every day. I love cartoons. I have dinner and before I go to bed my mum normally tells me I (7) *should/can't* read some of my library book. I (8) *don't have to/shouldn't* read it every day but I (9) *have to/can't* finish one book a week and write about it afterwards. I go to bed at about nine thirty. I (10) *should/can* go to bed earlier because I'm tired in the mornings. My mum reads me a story and my dad kisses me good night and I go to sleep.

5 Correct the mistakes in these sentences.

1 I can't to swim very well.
2 He shoulds do his homework before this afternoon.
3 Can't you tell me the time?
4 I haven't to go to school on Friday afternoon.
5 They don't can sing very well.
6 I should to ring him tomorrow.
7 Do you can play a musical instrument?
8 We has to work very hard at the moment.

Pronunciation | connected speech (2)

6 **a** 🔘 15 Listen and mark the sentences with a ✓ if the final *t* of *can't* and *shouldn't* is pronounced.

1 You shouldn't play with the football inside.
2 You shouldn't eat with your elbows on the table.
3 You can't complain about that.
4 You can't ask him the time in the exam.
5 You shouldn't walk round with no shoes on.
6 You can't ignore the teacher.
7 You can't answer the phone at the moment.
8 You shouldn't open the door when it's so cold.
9 You shouldn't sit so near the TV.

b Listen again and practise saying the sentences.

How to... | exchange opinions

7 Complete the dialogue with the words from the box.

> agree   opinion   reason   right   think
> so   sure (x2)

A: In my (1) _____ in this country it is impossible for women to get top jobs in companies. And the main (2) _____ for this is that men don't want women to get these jobs. Don't you think (3) _____ ?

B: I'm not so (4) _____ about that. There are some women in top jobs. And there are more women who go to university than men. What do you (5) _____ ?

A: I (6) _____ with you that there are more women studying at university than men. But I think it is more difficult for women to get top jobs when they finish university.

B: I think you're (7) _____ . Women don't get the top jobs, but I'm not so (8) _____ that men don't want them to get these jobs. I think there are more reasons for this.

Reading

1 **a** Read the texts. Write C (Carnegie), S (Soros), CS (both of them) or N (neither of them) next to the questions below.

1 Who left his country when he was a teenager?
2 Who had a good education?
3 Which of them made his money in the US?
4 Which of them worked in politics?
5 Who created new institutions to help people?
6 Who gave money to improve education?
7 Who returned to his home country to live?
8 Who wrote books?

Friends of the World

Andrew Carnegie

1 Andrew Carnegie was born in
Scotland in 1835. His family was
very poor. When Carnegie was
thirteen years old the family moved
5 to Pittsburgh in the US. He didn't
finish his education, but a rich man
called James Anderson gave Carnegie
books from his library. As a young
man, Carnegie worked on the railway. He invested his money in
10 business and made money quickly. In 1873 he started his own steel
company. By 1900 the company was producing twenty-five percent
of the steel in the US. There were no free public libraries in the
US so Carnegie built 2,800 of them. He also gave a lot of money
to charity. Finally he returned to Scotland, where he wrote several
15 books. He gave away ninety percent of his money and died in 1919.

George Soros

George Soros was born in Budapest, Hungary, in 1930. An
intelligent young man, Soros went to England in 1947 and studied
at the London School of Economics. Nine years later he went to
20 the US. Soros started an international investment company and
became rich quickly. He understood
international financial markets, and
was called, 'the man who broke the
Bank of England' when, in 1992, he
25 earned $1.1 billion in one day.
Soros created institutions to solve
world problems in health, education,
the media and human rights. These
institutions cost $400 million a
30 year. Soros now writes books about
politics, economics and society.

b Find words (1–4) in the
text. Match them to the correct
definitions (a–d) below.

1 invest in (v) (line 9)
2 charity (n) (line 14)
3 institution (n) (line 26)
4 human rights (n) (line 28)

a a big organisation
b put money into a business
c an organisation that gives
   money or things to people
   who need help
d things that everyone should
   be free to do/have

Grammar | Present Perfect Simple: *for* and *since*

2 Write *f* beside the
expressions we use with *for*
and *s* beside the expressions
we use with *since*.

a week	☐
10:30	☐
half an hour	☐
I last saw her	☐
then	☐
a long time	☐
a while	☐
1996	☐
this morning	☐
I left school	☐
three years	☐
we met	☐
ages	☐

3 Add one word to complete
each sentence.

1 I haven't been to the city
  centre ages.
2 She's lived there 1998.
3 I've worked in the shop a
  few years.
4 I haven't seen him I was at
  school.
5 She's played tennis she was
  a child.
6 I've known them last year.
7 Has he played on the team
  a long time?
8 He's taught at the school
  2006.

4 Complete the dialogue from a job interview with the Past Simple or the Present Perfect.

A: How long *have you worked* (you/work) with computers?

B: Well, I (1) _____ (work) with computers since 2004 when I (2) _____ (get) a job in Edinburgh.

A: How long (3) _____ (you/live) in Edinburgh?

B: I lived there for two years. In 2006 I (4) _____ (move) to Munich where I worked in a bank. I liked Munich but wanted to be near my family so I (5) _____ (come) back to London and I (6) _____ (live) here for the last three years.

A: How long have you worked in your present job?

B: I (7) _____ (work) in this company for three years now.

A: Is it a problem for you to move to Cardiff for this job?

B: Well, my parents (8) _____ (buy) a house in Cardiff last year so that isn't a problem. I'm happy to move here.

5 Write sentences with the same meaning. Use the words in brackets. Write 2–5 words.

1 I arrived in China last Thursday.
(here)
I've been _____ Thursday.

2 It is 2010. She first lived here in 2005.
(lived)
She _____ five years.

3 I met John at school. He's my best friend.
(known)
I've _____ we were at school.

4 I last saw Giorgio seven days ago.
(haven't)
I _____ last week.

5 I first played tennis in 1990 and I still play now.
(have)
I _____ 1990.

6 We arrived at 6.00 a.m. and it's now 9.00 a.m.!
(been)
We _____ three hours!

7 I'm a poet. I wrote my first poem years ago.
(poetry)
I've _____ a long time.

Vocabulary | friendship

6 Choose the correct verbs.

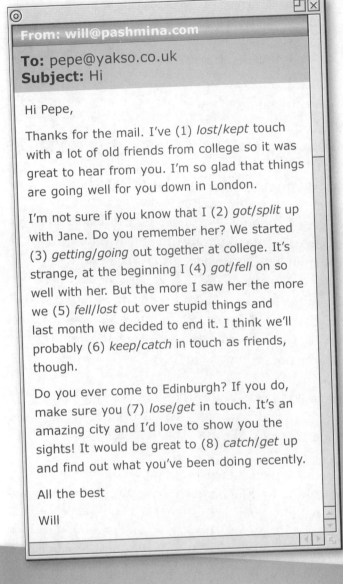

From: will@pashmina.com
To: pepe@yakso.co.uk
Subject: Hi

Hi Pepe,

Thanks for the mail. I've (1) *lost/kept* touch with a lot of old friends from college so it was great to hear from you. I'm so glad that things are going well for you down in London.

I'm not sure if you know that I (2) *got/split* up with Jane. Do you remember her? We started (3) *getting/going* out together at college. It's strange, at the beginning I (4) *got/fell* on so well with her. But the more I saw her the more we (5) *fell/lost* out over stupid things and last month we decided to end it. I think we'll probably (6) *keep/catch* in touch as friends, though.

Do you ever come to Edinburgh? If you do, make sure you (7) *lose/get* in touch. It's an amazing city and I'd love to show you the sights! It would be great to (8) *catch/get* up and find out what you've been doing recently.

All the best

Will

Reading

1 **a** Read the text and choose the best title.

- Ten Ways to Live Happily
- A Long, Long Life
- Jeanne Calment's Lawyer

Jeanne Calment was born in 1875 and died in 1997. At 122 years old, she was the world's oldest person.

She was born in Arles and became a celebrity in her home town. Journalists asked her about the secrets of her long life. She told them she used to eat chocolate and put olive oil on her skin. But the truth, her doctor said, is that she never felt stressed. She once said, 'If you can't do anything about it, why worry about it?' She also had a good sense of humour. When one visitor said to her, 'Maybe see you next year,' she replied, 'I don't see why not. You don't look so bad to me.'

She used to ride a bike (she stopped when she was 100), and her mind was strong even after her body grew old. She said, 'I never get bored.'

The best true Calment story was about her house. When she was 90, her lawyer bought the house. He paid her only $400 a month, a very small amount of money. His plan was to get the house when Jeanne Calment died. But he died first, aged 77, after paying $180,000, much more than the house was worth!

b Cover the text. Match a word from A to a word from B to make phrases from the text.

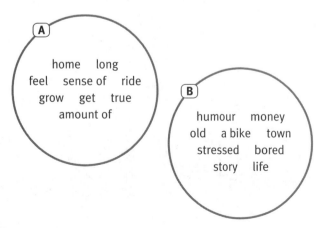

A
home   long
feel   sense of   ride
grow   get   true
amount of

B
humour   money
old   a bike   town
stressed   bored
story   life

c Use the phrases in exercise 1b to complete the summary. You may need to change the verb form.

1 She is famous because she lived a _____ _____ .

2 She died in her _____ _____ , Arles.

3 She never _____ _____ .

4 She had a good _____ _____ _____ .

5 She _____ _____ _____ until she was 100.

6 Her mind stayed young even when her body _____ _____ .

7 There is a funny _____ _____ about her house and her lawyer.

8 Her lawyer thought he would pay her a small _____ _____ _____ for the house. He was wrong!

Vocabulary | habits

2 Complete the sentences and write the words in the puzzle. Find the key word.

1 A: Do you always eat good food, like fruit and vegetables?
   B: Yes. I like to eat _____*ly*.

2 A: Do you always eat hamburgers, chips and chocolate?
   B: Yes. I love eating junk f_____ !

3 A: Do you smoke forty cigarettes a day?
   B: Yes. I'm a heavy _____r. I'm going to quit.

4 A: Do you go to gym every day?
   B: Yes. I love doing _____al exercise.

5 A: Do you like reading, playing chess and doing crosswords?
   B: Yes. I like to be mentally a_____ .

6 A: Do you worry about problems at work?
   B: Yes. I get really s_____ .

7 A: Do you always carry bottles in your bag?
   B: Yes. I drink a lot of w_____ .

8 A: Do you always feel good about life?
   B: Yes. I always think p_____y.

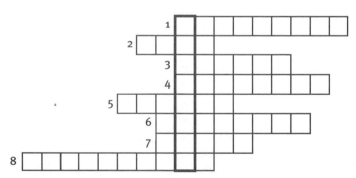

Grammar | *used to*: past habits

3 **a** Write *Yes/No* questions using *used to* and the prompts.

1 play/football on Saturdays
2 wear/uniform at school
3 get/good marks
4 eat/fast food
5 travel/for work

b Put the words in the correct order to make sentences with *used to*.

a Yes, I to good school marks used in my when I was get exams at.
b No, I to wear use one didn't.
c No, to eat vegetables fruit and I only used.
d No, never I to travel used for work.
e Yes, Saturday used every to play I.

c Match the questions in exercise 2a with the answers in exercise 2b.

Listening

4 🔘 16 Cover the audioscript. Listen to the interview with Angie about life in Britain in the 1950s and mark the sentences true (T) or false (F).

1 A lot of houses didn't have telephones.
2 Angie's mum used to wash clothes by hand.
3 There were a lot of big supermarkets.
4 Angie sometimes listened to records.
5 Angie played with computer games.
6 Clothes were less formal in the 1950s.

AUDIOSCRIPT

Presenter: Life has changed a lot since the 1950s. Then there was no Internet or mobile phones. But was there any technology then? What was life really like in Britain in the 50s? Today we're going to talk to Angie Parnwell, who was a teenager in the 1950s. Angie, what do you remember about technology in the 50s?

Angie: Well, there was technology in the 1950s but it was basic. Most houses didn't use to have telephones but there were cookers and radios – although in my house we didn't have a radio. My mum used to do the washing by hand as we didn't have a washing machine. There weren't big supermarkets either so when people went shopping they used to go to lots of different shops to get their food. My mum and dad used to take a long time to go round all the shops!

Presenter: And what about free time?

Angie: Well, people spent their free time in a different way too as there were no home computers and people didn't use to watch a lot of television. If we wanted to listen to music we had a record player. Children didn't have computer games so we spent a lot of time outside playing with our friends.

Presenter: And what did people wear back then?

Angie: Clothes were different too. The clothes I wore were more formal and less colourful. There were a lot of browns and greys in 1950s' clothes.

Presenter: Thanks Angie, That's been really interesting ...

Pronunciation | *used to/didn't used to*

5 🔘 17 Listen and repeat the sentences.

1 This used to be a school.
2 There didn't use to be a car park.
3 The museum used to be a hospital.
4 I used to come here to study.
5 Did there use to be a swimming pool?
6 There didn't use to be a hotel.

6 | Places

Vocabulary | places and geographical features

1 Read the text about Madrid and put the underlined words in the correct sentences.

The (1) population of Spain is Madrid. It is (2) capital in the centre of the country and it is one of the top tourist (3) remains in Europe. Madrid is an old city and archaeologists have found ancient (4) situated under the city. The mountains to the north of Madrid are in an area of great (5) destinations beauty and the (6) spaces to the south of Madrid is very flat. The (7) landscape of Madrid is between four and five million people. There are some beautiful green (8) natural in the city like the Retiro park.

2 Complete the sentences using the words in the box.

> bay   beaches   cliffs   coast   forest   island
> lake   mountain   peninsula   river   sea

1   Australia is the biggest _____ in the world.
2   The Nile is the longest _____ in the world.
3   The highest _____ in the Alps is Mont Blanc.
4   The mountains of Canada are covered in a thick _____ .
5   The long, white _____ in Brazil are beautiful.
6   The Caspian Sea is surrounded by land so it is, in fact, the world's biggest _____ .
7   The city of Odessa, Ukraine, is on the Black _____ .
8   There's a great view of the _____ from there – you can see the sea and the beach.
9   Spain and Portugal form the Iberian _____ .
10 Madagascar is a big island off the east _____ of Africa.
11 There are lots of tall, rocky _____ in the west of Ireland.

Grammar | will, may and might: prediction

3 Find the mistakes in five of the sentences and correct them.

1   I might to finish it later if I have time.
2   He willn't win the game tomorrow if he plays like that.
3   They may not buy the car this year – I don't think they have the money.
4   I might go not to the cinema this evening if there's a good film on.
5   I'm sure they may join the company next year.
6   I'm certain they'll win the league next year. They've got some great players.
7   I'll might start work early on Thursday.
8   I'm not certain but I might see her tomorrow.

4 Choose the correct alternative.

1   I am going out to lunch. *I see you/I'll see you* later.
2   The weather is getting better. I think *I'll go/I go* to the beach this weekend.
3   *Will you stay/Do you stay* in the same hotel when you come back next month?
4   I am very tired. *I'll finish/I finish* this report tomorrow.
5   Is that the phone ringing? *I'll get/I get* it.
6   I love sport. *I do/I'll do* lots of sports at weekends.
7   My mother is in hospital, so *I visit/I'll visit* her every day.
8   I haven't spoken to Jenny for ages. *I send/I'll send* her a postcard.

Pronunciation | contractions: will

5 **a** Mark the contractions in these sentences.

I will see you on Monday!

I'*ll* see you on Monday!

1   It will be cold again tomorrow.
2   They will eat a lot more on holiday.
3   I will have the club sandwich.
4   She will be here at about 9:30.
5   I think you will pass the exam easily.
6   He will be lucky if he gets good weather in Scotland.

b 18 Listen and check your answers. Practise saying the sentences.

Reading

6 **a** You are going to read about two tourist destinations: Switzerland and Western Australia. Before you read, answer the questions (1–5). Write S if you think the answer is Switzerland or WA if you think the answer is Western Australia.

Where ...

1 do people speak different languages in different cities?
2 can you explore the desert?
3 can you find beautiful beaches?
4 can you visit lakes in the mountains?
5 can you swim with dolphins?

b Read the texts to check your answers.

7 Mark these sentences true (T), false (F) or no information (NI).

Switzerland

1 The north is more beautiful than the south.
2 The main language in Bern is German.
3 It's difficult to travel from one city to another city.

Western Australia

4 *Outback* is a town.
5 Perth is the capital of Western Australia.
6 There are a lot of pubs.

8 Phrases (1–6) in the text are useful ways of describing a tourist destination. Match (1–6) to a similar phrase (a–f) below.

a It's a good idea to start your holiday ...
b well-known because of ...
c In the south/east/west ...
d Visit ... in order to ...
e There are some very famous/beautiful/expensive places. This is one of them.
f Tourists like to visit this place all year.

Switzerland is (1) *one of Europe's most* beautiful countries. Cities like Zurich seem like a concrete jungle, and then you look up and see the wonderful mountains of the Alps. (2) *In the north* the landscape has a natural beauty, with green fields and villages which look like the pictures on a chocolate box. Each of Switzerland's main cities has a different character, from French-speaking Geneva to German Bern to Italian Lugano. Swiss people (3) *are famous for* their efficiency, so travelling around the country is easy. Switzerland's beautiful lakes, clean air, and fields full of flowers (4) *attract visitors throughout the year.*

Western Australia

Sun, adventure, a beautiful environment and friendly people. This is what you'll find on a holiday to Western Australia.

Western Australia has a natural beauty, long days of sunshine, clear blue skies, and fantastic beaches. (5) *Come to Western Australia to* swim with wild dolphins, walk through the ancient forest, or sleep under the stars in the Outback desert. (6) *Why not start your holiday* in the capital city of Western Australia, Perth? You can spend an afternoon sitting outside a pub and enjoying a cool drink with the locals.

Listening

1 🔘 19 Cover the audioscript. Listen to the dialogue between James and Anna about the film *Invictus*. Mark the sentences J if James gives the opinion, A if Anna gives the opion or B if both of them give the opinion.

1 Morgan Freeman was excellent in the film.
2 Matt Damon doesn't act very well.
3 Matt Damon does a good South African accent.
4 It is difficult for an actor to act as a sportsman.
5 Matt Damon went to the gym to prepare for the film.
6 It's an amazing story.
7 Clint Eastwood is a great director.

AUDIOSCRIPT

James: Have you seen the Clint Eastwood film about Mandela and the Rugby World Cup?

Anna: Yeah, I saw it last week.

James: I just saw it yesterday. What did you think?

Anna: Well, I didn't know anything about the Rugby World Cup and the film taught me a lot about that and about South Africa. For instance, I didn't know that rugby was really only played by whites and that there was only one black player on the national team at the time.

James: Yeah, Chester Williams. And he nearly missed the match because he was injured.

Anna: It's such a great story! And I thought Morgan Freeman was excellent as usual.

James: I think so too. I think he was very convincing as Mandela. What did you think of Matt Damon as Pienaar, the rugby captain?

Anna: Well, in my opinion this was the weak part of the film. Well, I don't think Damon acts very well in the film. He doesn't seem very real as a rugby player.

James: I don't agree. I think it is very difficult to act as a sportsman if you aren't one. And I think he does an OK job. And his South African accent is very good.

Anna: Well, I'm not sure I agree with you there, but he does look very big in the film.

James: Yes, apparently he was in the gym a lot before he started acting.

Anna: The thing that I though was most incredible was the fact that South Africa won the World Cup as well, when most people thought they weren't going to win. It's an amazing story.

James: Yes, absolutely amazing ...

Anna: And Clint Eastwood is a great director. I wonder what his next film will be about.

Grammar | countable and uncountable nouns

2 Complete the sentences using the words in the box.

> a few   many   any (x2)   some   much   a little
> a lot of (x2)

1 They aren't doing anything because they haven't got _____ work at the moment.
2 There aren't _____ people in the library today. I can only see three or four students.
3 Are there _____ vegetables in your garden or are there only flowers?
4 Does your garden get _____ sunshine?
5 For a small plant you only need _____ soil.
6 He must have _____ money – he's got a great house and a really expensive car.
7 It's a very small prison – there are only _____ prisoners here.
8 The baby elephant needs to eat _____ food to grow normally.
9 I need to go to the bank to get _____ money.

3 Tom is asking Ailsa about the ingredients he needs to make a Spanish omelette. Read the conversation and choose the correct alternative.

Tom: So if I'm going to make a Spanish omelette, what do I need?

Ailsa: You need (1) *some/much* eggs and a (2) *little/few* salt. You also need quite (3) *a lot of/many* potatoes if you want to make a big omelette but only a (4) *little/few* if it is going to be a small one.

Tom: Have you got (5) *any/much* eggs?

Ailsa: You might want to get some more. Oh and I don't have (6) *many/much* potatoes, so you'll have to buy some.

Tom: What about milk?

Ailsa: Some people like to add a (7) *little/few* milk. I haven't got (8) *much/many* milk so maybe buy a litre or two. Oh and if you like, you can get a (9) *few/little* onions – it's delicious if you add them in.

4 Underline the alternative which is not possible.

1 I did *a lot of/some/many* work today.

2 I haven't got *much/many/any* money.

3 Can you give me *a few/some/a little bit* of advice?

4 I found *some/a lot of/a bit* information on the Internet.

5 There aren't *many/some/any* animals in this circus.

6 I got *some/a/the* job.

7 We're buying *some/a lot of/many* furniture tomorrow.

8 Have you heard *any/the/a few* news?

9 We didn't eat *any/much/many* chocolate last Christmas.

10 I haven't spoken to *a lot of/many/much* people today.

Vocabulary | describing a place

5 **a** Put the underlined letters in the correct order to make a word.

1 I went on a <u>matironc</u> holiday last weekend with my husband.

2 It's a totally <u>oilunpst</u> place – there are no buildings or roads at all.

3 The area round the lake was so quiet and <u>fupaecel</u>.

4 I think it's the perfect place to go on holiday – just <u>llyidic</u>.

5 It's a really <u>cwderod</u> bar. There are far too many people there.

6 They said it was a lovely hotel but very <u>oinys</u>. They could hear the traffic all night.

7 When I'm really busy and stressed I often go on a <u>rxinelag</u> weekend in the country.

8 It's a really <u>inecixtg</u> city – there's so much to do and see!

9 It's a <u>ebifuautl</u> part of the country, with lovely mountains and lakes.

10 The river is very <u>mpsiresive</u>, it's so fast and wide here.

11 It's a really <u>asplaent</u> place to eat outside beside the river.

12 It's a really <u>lwid</u> part of the country, there are no houses or buildings near.

b Complete the text below with the best words from exercise 5a.

I've lived in lots of different places, in the city and out in the countryside. The first place I bought was actually a flat, right in the centre of London. A great place to live but I found it difficult to get to sleep at night because it was so (1) _____.
I loved it though, London is a really fast-moving, (2) _____ city and the buildings and monuments are really (3) _____.
There are so many people in the streets that it sometimes feels too (4) _____ but it is still my favourite city. Anyway, I lived in London for a few years and then decided to move out to the country because I needed to live somewhere quieter and more (5) _____ as I needed to concentrate on my writing.
I found a cottage in an (6) _____ valley with no other houses around. The valley was really (7) _____ – it had lovely trees and fields. It was so (8) _____ after the stress of the big city. The countryside and mountains around the house were very (9) _____ and even a bit dangerous to walk in on your own, especially in winter. But in summer it was really (10) _____ in the evenings to sit outside and watch the sun go down. After two years there I moved back to the city, Manchester this time but I kept the cottage in the country.
I still go there sometimes with my wife for (11) _____ weekends. At the moment I'm trying to buy another house, but this time by the sea. I want to find an (12) _____ place near the ocean but it's very expensive.

c Make a list of places in your country which could be could be described by the adjectives from exercise 5a.

Pronunciation | dipthongs

6 **a** Look at the underlined sounds in these words and write the words in the correct columns.

<u>a</u>rea cr<u>ow</u>ded disapp<u>ear</u> exc<u>i</u>ting l<u>o</u>cal pl<u>a</u>ce
t<u>ou</u>r unsp<u>oi</u>lt

/eɪ/	/aɪ/	/ɔɪ/	/əʊ/	/aʊ/	/ɪə/	/eə/	/ʊə/

b ● 20 Listen and check your answers. Repeat the words.

6.3

Vocabulary | urban environment

1 Choose the correct alternative.

1 I go to the *sports stadium/leisure centre* every week to an aerobics class.

2 My wife bought me the book in the local *library/book shop*.

3 I had a great three course lunch in the Italian *restaurant/café* yesterday.

4 She was dancing in the *bar/nightclub* till three in the morning.

5 After the accident he was taken to the emergency ward at the *hospital/doctor's surgery*.

6 'Have you seen what films are on at the *cinema/theatre* this week?'

7 There's an exhibition of paintings on at the town *museum/art gallery*.

8 I started *school/college* at 9:00 a.m. when I was ten.

2 Put the correct words in the crossword using the clues below.

A place where ...

Across

1 ... you study when you finish school.

2 ... big sports events are held. *sports stadium*

3 ... you can see a play.

4 ... you can buy alcoholic drinks.

Down

5 ... you can see a doctor. *doctor's surgery*

6 ... people catch a bus at the side of the road.

7 ... trains arrive and leave from.

8 ... you can get tea or coffee, drinks and snacks.

9 ... you can borrow books.

10 ... you can see historical or scientific objects.

```
        ⁵d
         o
        ¹c □ □ □ □ □
         t
         o
         r
         s            ⁸□   ⁹□
⁶□     ²s p o r t s ⁷s t a d i u ¹⁰m
         u
         r
         g
³□ □ □ □  e □ □ □ □      ⁴□ □ □ □
         r
         y
```

Grammar | *too, too much/many, (not) enough*

3 Complete the sentences using *too, too much, too many* or *enough*.

1 It's _____ crowded for me in the city. I prefer the country.

2 There are _____ people on the beach today.

3 There aren't _____ buses. We always have to wait.

4 There is _____ noise in here. I'm going to work next door.

5 It's _____ hot in the office. Can you turn on the air-conditioning?

6 I'm sorry, but I didn't have _____ money to buy you a drink.

7 I have got _____ homework to do. I'll never finish it by tomorrow!

8 There are _____ TV channels. I can never decide which one to watch.

4 Look at the pictures. Complete the sentences using *too* or *enough* and words from the box.

> crowded   loud   money   small   suitcases   tall

1 The music is _____ _____.

2 He isn't _____ _____.

3 They have got _____ many _____.

4 He hasn't got _____ _____ to buy food.

5 The train is _____ _____.

6 His jacket is _____ _____ for him.

5 Complete the sentences using *too*, *enough*, *too many*, *too much* and the words in brackets.

1 I'm not going to play football tonight. I'm _____ . (tired)

2 You are not working _____ . You won't pass your exams. (hard)

3 He spends _____ on the computer. He never goes out. (time)

4 We would like to buy a new car, but it is _____ . (expensive)

5 Those children eat _____ . It's not good for them. (hamburgers)

6 I want to write to them in Russian, but my Russian is not _____ . (good)

7 The film was really boring. It was _____ . (long)

8 We didn't go into the museum, because there were _____ . (people)

9 I can't speak to her now. I am _____ . (busy)

10 You can't come into this club. You are not _____ . (old)

Reading

6 Read the interview about the perfect city and mark the sentences true (T), false (F) or no information (NI).

1 The perfect city is not by the sea.

2 There should be places for people to ice-skate in the city in the winter.

3 There are small avenues in the perfect city.

4 In the perfect city you can pay for bicycles on the corner of big streets.

5 The perfect city has an airport quite near the centre.

6 Restaurants in the perfect city should only offer food from the country the city is in.

7 A perfect city has lots of big sports stadiums.

Interviewer: The perfect city doesn't exist. But if you *could* design the perfect city, what would it be like? Well here to tell us is Sean Richards, an expert on town planning. Sean, tell us about the perfect city.

Sean: Well, first of all it would be on the coast. There are some great cities which are not by the sea, but in general people love the influence the sea brings to a city. They also love being able to go to the beach! It would also have mountains nearby – great for walking trips or even skiing in the winter.

Interviewer: OK, that is the location. But what does it look like?

Sean: The perfect city should be a mix of big wide avenues and small, old side streets. It should also have squares for people to sit down and enjoy a drink in the sunshine. In the perfect city I'd like areas only for pedestrians, if possible in the city centre. Apart from streets for cars, cities should have wide pavements for people to walk down and bicycle paths for people to cycle on. There should be free bicycles too, which people can collect at the corner of big streets – because cycling is a cheap and healthy way to travel. An underground train and a good bus service are also vital because people need to be able to travel quickly to their jobs. There should be an airport a maximum of thirty minutes from the city centre.

Interviewer: And what about entertainment in the city?

Sean: Well, a perfect city must have museums and art galleries with important works of art. I'd also need theatres and cinemas, pubs and restaurants which offer different types of cuisine from all over the world. There should be green spaces too, with lots of areas for children to play in and places for people to play sports in too.

Interviewer: OK, Sean, just one question. Is all this possible?

Sean: Perhaps not, but you all probably know a city with at least some of these characteristics.

Review and consolidation 4–6

Comparative and superlative adjectives

1 Complete the sentences using the adjectives in brackets. Use a comparative or superlative.

1 Malawi is _____ (hot) than Iceland.
2 Wolves are _____ (dangerous) than dogs.
3 Elephants are _____ (large) land mammals in the world.
4 Russ is _____ (young) than me.
5 The Psychology course is _____ (interesting) the History course.
6 *Casablanca* is _____ (romantic) film I've ever seen.
7 The Karoo Desert is _____ (small) than the Sahara.
8 That was _____ (good) day of my life.
9 Sarah is _____ (lazy) than her sister.
10 Ling bought _____ (pretty) dress in the shop.
11 My old teacher was _____ (kind) than the new one.
12 He's _____ (fast) runner in our team.

Indirect questions

2 Put the words in the correct order to make questions.

1 me what leaves time you tell the can train?
2 the do you pharmacy is know where?
3 know where do you I can a bus buy ticket?
4 time me starts what the can you tell film?
5 you desk do where the know information is?
6 tell this gate me how can you I open can?
7 tell time me the can you?
8 tell the station us how to can you get to?
9 do she you know where works?
10 me are how much can you tell the stamps?

should, can, have to: obligation and permission

3 Make sentences with the same meaning. Use the words in brackets. Write 2–3 words.

1 It's a good idea to buy our tickets early.
   We _____ our tickets early. (should)
2 It isn't necessary to pay for children.
   You _____ pay for children. (have)
3 She needs to do her exam again.
   She _____ her exam again. (has)
4 Is it possible for me to go home now?
   _____ home now? (Can)
5 It's not a good idea to arrive late.
   We _____ late. (shouldn't)
6 She doesn't know how to drive.
   She _____ . (can't)
7 Is it necessary to read this book?
   Do we _____ this book? (have)
8 It's healthy to eat more vegetables.
   You _____ more vegetables. (should)
9 Is it necessary for me to leave?
   Do _____ leave? (have)
10 I know how to fly an aeroplane.
   I _____ an aeroplane. (can)

used to and Present Perfect with for and since

4 Complete the sentences with *used to* and the words in brackets. Then match to a–e and choose *for* or *since*.

1 I _____ (eat) junk food
2 She _____ (be) good at the guitar
3 We _____ (not/like) each other when we were children
4 Mum and Dad _____ (travel) a lot
5 I _____ (not/cook) much pasta

a but we've been friends *for/since* the last few months.
b but I've eaten a lot of it *for/since* I went to Italy.
c but I have been much healthier *for/since* last year.
d but they haven't had a holiday *for/since* 2005.
e but she hasn't played *for/since* two years.

will, may and might with too, too much/many, (not) enough

5 Complete the sentences using will/won't/may and might and circle the correct word.

1 I _____ go to the cinema if there aren't *enough/too many* people in the queue.

2 I'm not sure – I _____ see you tomorrow if it's not *too/too much* cold.

3 She _____ go to university if her marks are good *enough/too much*.

4 I'm certain they _____ take a taxi – it won't cost *too much/too many*.

5 I'm sure she _____ change her job because she doesn't earn *too/enough* money.

6 My new flat is close *enough/too* to my office, so I _____ need to drive to work.

7 He's not sure, he _____ move house next year – where he lives is *too/enough* small.

8 She _____ stay in this hotel because it's *too/enough* expensive.

9 We _____ be able to go swimming today because the water is *enough/too* cold.

10 There is *too many/too much* traffic here, you _____ be able to see his car.

Countable and uncountable nouns

6 Correct the mistakes in the sentences.

1 I don't have many money left this month.

2 We need a few orange juice for breakfast.

3 Have you got an oranges?

4 We don't know much people in the area yet.

5 There isn't a modern equipment on the farm.

6 Do you have a bit of trees in your garden?

7 In the morning the garden gets a bit sunshine.

8 Normally there are only a little people in the café at lunchtime.

9 Have you got many time after dinner to do your homework?

10 Can I have a few water please?

Vocabulary

7 Complete the text with the verbs from the box. You may have to change the tense of the verbs.

> achieve control cope earn get (x2)
> graduate learn think

When I (1) _____ from university I wanted to (2) _____ a job in teaching. What was most important for me was to (3) _____ a good salary so that I could leave home and (4) _____ a place of my own. I also wanted to (5) _____ to drive a car so I definitely needed a well-paid job. I started a teacher training course which was very intensive and I had to (6) _____ with a lot of problems. The first classes I taught were with very difficult teenagers and I actually had to (7) _____ my fear and (8) _____ positively before I went into the classroom. Anyway, I kept working hard and in the end I (9) _____ my goal and became a teacher.

8 Write a word from Units 4, 5 or 6 to match the definitions. The first letter of each word is supplied.

1 *a*_____ (n) a young person who is between a child and an adult (Unit 5.1)

2 *b*_____ (adj) isn't afraid of anything (4.1)

3 *c*_____ (n) the area of land by the sea (6.1)

4 *d*_____ (n) tourist … a place where tourists go (6.1)

5 *e*_____ (adj) old (5.1)

6 *f*_____ (adj) physically healthy and strong because of exercise (4.1)

7 *g*_____ (n) art … a place where you can see exhibitions of paintings (6.3)

8 *h*_____ (adv) If you eat …, you eat food which is good for you (5.3)

9 *i*_____ area (adj) a place with factories and businesses (6.3)

10 *j*_____ (adj) … food = eaten in fast food restaurants (5.3)

11 *k*_____ (v) … in touch, to stay in contact with someone (5.2)

12 *l*_____ centre (n) = place with a swimming pool and facilities for sports (6.3)

13 *m*_____ (adj) keen and interested (4.1)

14 *n*_____ (n) a place where you can drink and dance until late (6.3)

15 *o*_____ (prep) get … well with = have a good relationship with (5.2)

16 *p*_____ (n) long piece of land which sticks out into the sea or a lake (6.1)

17 *r*_____ (n) old ruins of buildings (6.1)

18 *s*_____ (n) protection from the weather and animals (4.2)

19 *t*_____ (n) a young child who is learning to walk (5.1)

20 *u*_____ (adj) a natural place without buildings (6.2)

21 *v*_____ (n) you can grow them in a garden (6.2)

22 *w*_____ (n) undeveloped, natural place (4.2)

23 *y*_____ (adj) not old (5.1)

7 | Body

Vocabulary | appearance

1 Put the letters in the correct order to make words to label the pictures.

1 twias _____   8 neke _____
2 dohulers _____   9 ginfre _____
3 blewo _____   10 efheaord _____
4 rwsit _____   11 knael _____
5 rae _____   12 yee _____
6 seon _____   13 tumoh _____
7 kacb _____   14 ahri _____

2 a Match the words to make complete phrases.

1 physical   a like
2 get   b appearance
3 go on   c weight
4 look   d stressed
5 put on   e a diet

b Complete the sentences with the correct phrases from exercise 2a. You may need to change the form of the verb.

1 I'm sure she's _____ . She looks fatter than she used to.
2 When there are problems at work I _____ . I need to relax more.
3 He's so handsome, he _____ Brad Pitt!
4 He _____ and lost a lot of weight.
5 She's obsessed with her _____ . She's always looking in the mirror.

3 Match the words (1–7) with their opposites (a–g).

1 tall   a overweight
2 dark-skinned   b short
3 ugly   c fair-skinned
4 fat   d dark-haired
5 beautiful/handsome e skinny
6 fair-haired   f good-looking
7 slim   g unattractive

Grammar | First Conditional

4 Complete the sentences with phrases from the box.

> we'll talk about it later.
> I'll buy you a copy for your birthday.
> we'll celebrate with a party.
> I'll go to the bank and get some.
> will you come?   we'll stay in and eat pizza.
> there won't be any left.

1 If you pass your exams,
2 If you don't want to come out tonight,
3 If you need some more money,
4 If you like that CD,
5 If you're too busy now,
6 If we don't buy tickets soon,
7 If I invite you to the party,

5 Choose the correct alternative.

1 If you *see/will see* Max, *will you/do you* tell him I want to talk to him?
2 If they *won't come/don't come* home soon, their dinner *will be/is* cold.
3 Your mother *will be/is* worried if you *don't call/won't call* her.
4 If you *don't leave/won't leave* now, you*'ll miss/miss* the train.
5 Your manager *won't be/is not* very happy if you *will go/go* to work in those clothes.
6 If we *find/will find* a nice restaurant, we*'ll tell/we tell* you about it.
7 We*'ll be/are* in New York by 8 o'clock if there *aren't/won't be* any problems.
8 If you *don't sleep/won't sleep* well tonight, you *won't feel/do not feel* good in the morning.

44

6 Pete and Shaune are going to a health farm. Complete the sentences using the prompts.

1 If Pete/do/lots of exercise/his muscles/get stronger

_____

2 If Shaune/do yoga/she/feel happier

_____

3 Their skin/look better/if they/drink/lots of water

_____

4 They/feel/more relaxed/if they/have/massages every day

_____

5 If Shaune/eat salads/for a week/she/lose weight

_____

6 They/not feel/so tired/if they/sleep/for ten hours a day

_____

7 If they/not eat junk food/for a week/they/feel healthier

_____

8 They/be/less stressed/if they/not think/about work

_____

9 If Pete/lose weight/he/have/more energy

_____

10 If they/stay/health farm/too long/they/ healthier/poorer!

_____

7 Correct the mistakes in these sentences.

1 If I'll pass the exam, I'll get the place at university I want.
2 I ring you tomorrow, if I see him.
3 We'll get a new car if he got a new job.
4 They'll won't be happy if they don't go to the party.
5 You see her on the news if you'll turn on the TV at 9:00.
6 You won't be cold you take your jacket.
7 I'll can use the computer programme if you teach me.
8 If you see him tomorrow, you'll tell him the news?

Pronunciation | intonation in conditional clauses

8 a 🔘 21 Listen and mark these sentences with arrows to show where the intonation goes up (⟋), down (⟍) or stays the same (→).

If you stay in the sun too long, you'll burn.

1 I'll do it tomorrow if I have time.
2 We'll take you home by car if you stay for the match.
3 They will be very angry if they see the rubbish on the floor.
4 If you get to work late, you'll have to leave later.
5 If we take the train, we'll be there by five thirty.

b Listen again and repeat the sentences.

Lifelong learning | remembering words

9 Look at the sets of words (1–5). Match them with the different ways of grouping to help remember words (a–e).

1 investigation, education, participation, situation
2 waiter, customer, menu, bill
3 attractive, good-looking, handsome, pretty
4 short, thin, dark-haired, attractive
5 small, short, slim, skinny

a by topic/meaning
b by first letter
c by part of speech/similar endings
d by creating a story
e by drawing a network

New Internet design company is looking for a young, (1) _____ (wants success) person to help us increase business in our second year.

Friendly, (2) _____ (easy to talk to and talks a lot) waitress needed for local café. Experience an advantage

Nurses needed to help look after old people in their homes. You should be (3) _____ (good at planning and doing things you have to do) and (4) _____ (think about how other people will feel*).

We are looking for a new gardener. Must be (5) _____ (wants to work hard).

University library needs assistant. The job is good for a quiet, (8) _____ (does not talk about feelings) person.

Would you like to be on TV? Are you happy to talk about your relationships? We are looking for (6) _____ (happy to talk about feelings) people to be part of a new TV show. No (7) _____ (doesn't do what he/she should do) people, please.

* this word also means 'easily upset'

Vocabulary | personality

1 Complete the job adverts using words from the box. One of the words is not needed.

> ambitious   chatty   easy-going   hard-working
> lazy   open   organised   reserved   sensitive
> unreliable

Pronunciation | schwa /ə/ on unstressed syllables

2 a 🔘 22 Listen and underline the words pronounced with a schwa.

1 happy to talk about feelings
2 make lots of lists and plans
3 are easy to talk to and talk a lot
4 don't talk about feelings or problems
5 really want to be successful
6 not easily annoyed or worried by things
7 don't like work or physical activity

b Listen again to check your answers and repeat the phrases.

Grammar | gerunds and infinitives

3 Choose the correct alternative.

1 She seemed *to think/thinking* that the concert was yesterday.
2 I've enjoyed *to talk/talking* to you.
3 We can't avoid *to meet/meeting* him.
4 He offered *to take/taking* us to the station.
5 I can't imagine *to work/working* without a computer.
6 I've decided *to change/changing* my job.
7 We considered *to move/moving* to the US.
8 They didn't expect *to find/finding* you here.
9 Do you promise not *to tell/telling* anyone?
10 I miss *to see/seeing* the mountains.

4 Complete the story using the correct form of the verbs in brackets.

You will have a long life.

When a woman read my palm, I didn't expect (1) _____ (learn) anything new. I don't believe in things like that and I avoid (2) _____ (look at) my horoscope. Then I met a woman in a bar who offered (3) _____ (read) my palm. At first I didn't want her (4) _____ (do) it, but then I decided (5) _____ (try) it. She promised not (6) _____ (tell) me anything terrible. She told me about the problems I had at work. She told me that I wanted (7) _____ (change) things. I really enjoyed (8) _____ (listen) to her and she seemed (9) _____ (understand) me. Then she told me I would go on a journey which would change my life. I laughed because I couldn't afford (10) _____ (travel). Two weeks later I won a holiday to the Caribbean. Can you imagine (11) _____ (win) a holiday like that? Anyway I met my husband on that holiday, so it really did change my life! I have always wanted (12) _____ (say) thank you to that woman in the bar.

5 Find the mistakes in eight of the sentences (1–10) and correct them.

1 I am hoping to meeting the artist at the exhibition.
2 I miss to see my friends and family.
3 I expect you be here at 9 o'clock.
4 She offered to help me with the cooking.
5 He has decided taking a week off work.
6 We avoided to tell you earlier because of your exams.
7 You can't afford going out every night. It's too expensive.
8 I promised to going to her house this evening.
9 I want tell you what happened.
10 It seems to be the cheapest shop.

Reading

6 **a** Read the text and look at your own hand. Can you find the lines mentioned in the text on your palm?

b Mark the statements true (T) or false (F).

1 The left hand shows personality.
2 Palmists think that the life line shows physical health.
3 The life line can show an accident.
4 The heart line finishes under the thumb.
5 The head line is always separate from the life line.
6 The fate line represents things that the person controls.

c Correct the sentences which are false.

Palm Reading

First, which hand to read? Some people think that the left hand shows the potential of the person and the right shows the personality. Some people think it is better to read a woman's left hand and a man's right hand. Whichever hand you read, the most important thing to look for are lines. These are the most important lines: the life line, the heart line, the head line and the fate line.

The life line extends from the edge of the palm above the thumb and goes in a curve down to the wrist. Palmists (people who read palms) believe that this line represents the person's physical health and general well being. It can also show important events in a person's life, like an accident or a physical problem. A lot of palmists think that it shows how long a person will live.

The heart line is at the top of the palm, under the fingers. It normally finishes at the end of the palm under the little finger. Palmists think that this line represents the heart and it shows emotions and romance.

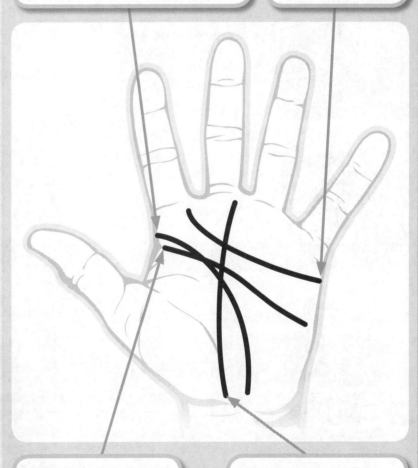

The head line starts at the end of the palm under the index finger and goes across the palm and normally finishes at halfway down the palm. Often the head line joins with the life line. This line represents the person's mind and the way it works.

Another important line is the fate line. It runs from the bottom of the palm near the wrist, up through the centre of the palm towards the middle finger. This line is connected to the life path. Some palmists think that this line reflects things that the person cannot control.

Vocabulary | illness

1 Use a word from A and a word from B to complete the sentences.

A	B
feel high neck sore (x2)	eyes hurts sick temperature wrist

1   I've got a very _____ _____ .

2   I've been looking at the computer too long and now I've got _____ _____ .

3   Yes, he has a _____ _____ .

4   I can't eat any more. I _____ _____ .

5   Doctor, my _____ really _____ .

2 Correct the mistakes in the sentences.

1   Have you got an aspirin? I feel a terrible headache.

2   I can't eat anything. I feel to be sick.

3   You don't look well. Are you a high temperature?

4   I ate too much chocolate and now I've got a stomachaches.

5   I'm going to try acupuncture for my backsache.

6   I don't feel very good. I've got cold.

7   I'm staying at home. I've feel the flu.

How to... | give and respond to advice

3 Look at the sentences in exercise 1. Match them with the pieces of advice (a–e).

a   You shouldn't have any more cake.

b   Why don't you close your eyes and have a rest?

c   He shouldn't go back to school yet.

d   You need to stop typing.

e   Have you tried putting ice on it?

Grammar | stop, try, remember with infinitives

4 Complete the text with the correct forms of the verbs in brackets.

When I was younger I don't remember ever (1) _____ (be) seriously ill. I was always playing sports so I was generally very healthy. In fact I played so many sports I never stopped (2) _____ (study) hard. I sometimes forgot my homework but I always remembered to put my football boots in my bag! But I did hurt my leg once playing football. I was running and I tried (3) _____ (stop) before I hit this big defender but I couldn't and I ran into him. I can remember (4) _____ (feel) a terrible pain in my leg and the trainer saying, 'I think he's broken his leg!' Afterwards my leg didn't feel strong and I tried (5) _____ (go) to the gym to get stronger. It didn't really work and I was never as good at football again.

5 Find the mistakes in four of the sentences and correct them.

1 Remember to buy some paracetamol before you come.
2 Why don't you try to take some honey and butter in hot milk?
3 I feel terrible. I can't stop to cough!
4 I remember taking days off school for illness when I was young.
5 Stop to go to the gym if you've hurt your leg!
6 I know you've got a lot of work but try to taking a break every few hours.

6 Complete these sentences so that they are true for you.

1 I have never tried ...
2 I stopped ...
3 I remember ...
4 I find it difficult to remember to ...
5 I once tried to ...
6 I stopped to ...

Listening

7 **a** 🔵 23 Cover the audioscript. Listen to the interview and answer the question.

Shiatsu is ...

A a type of Swiss massage.
B a Japanese medicine.
C a type of Japanese massage.
D a Chinese mushroom.

b Listen again and complete the notes in the table.

SHIATSU	
What are the main beliefs?	Like (1) _____ it believes that there are channels of (2) _____ .
Where is it from?	It is a (3) _____ massage.
What happens in a typical session?	• Firstly, the practitioner will (4) _____ about your health. • Then, he/she will give you a (5) _____ . • Lastly, he/she will (6) _____ points on your body.
What does it treat?	It is very good for (7) _____ , stomachaches and (8) _____ .
How long does it take?	A session takes about (9) _____ .
Do patients always feel better immediately?	(10) _____ . Sometimes it takes (11) _____ sessions.

AUDIOSCRIPT

Woman: So what is Shiatsu?

Man: Well, it's a type of massage. It's like acupuncture because it believes that there are channels of energy. You press on different points on the body and the energy moves around better.

Woman: I see. Where is it from?

Man: Shiatsu is a Japanese massage, but now you can have Shiatsu treatments in many countries.

Woman: Right. And what happens in a typical session?

Man: First, the Shiatsu practitioner asks you questions about your health, and your problem. Then he gives you a massage to relax the muscles. Lastly, he presses points on your body. He usually uses his hands, but sometimes he uses his arms, elbows, knees and feet.

Woman: His feet? OK. So what problems can it treat?

Man: It's very good for problems like backache, stomachache and headache, but it works for other problems too.

Woman: That's good. How long does it take?

Man: Each session usually takes about an hour.

Woman: An hour. And do patients feel better after one hour?

Man: Actually, no. Some patients will feel worse at the beginning. Sometimes they need two, three or more sessions before they feel better.

Vocabulary | speed

1 Match the sentence halves.

1 There was a speed
2 She's always in a
3 What's the speed
4 The car has a top
5 He didn't arrive on
6 I got caught in rush
7 You can take
8 Please slow
9 Can't you speed
10 I have to eat on the

a time – he was more than 10 minutes late.
b go today – I don't have time to sit down.
c hour traffic at six o'clock.
d your time, there's no rush.
e limit in your country on the motorway?
f hurry – she has no time for anything.
g speed of 180 mph.
h up? We'll never get there!
i down, you're driving too fast!
j camera on the bridge which caught me speeding.

2 Complete the text using the words from the box.

> behind   down   in   on   with   up (x2)

Are you always (1) _____ a hurry? Do you often get (2) _____ with your work? Do you have to stay late in the office to catch (3) _____ _____ your work? Do you panic when you can't arrive (4) _____ time? Why? Stop worrying! The world is 25 billion years old. It will continue with or without you. You need to slow (5) _____, not speed (6) _____! Join the Slow Living movement and see a better, slower world. Join today! Or tomorrow . . . or next week . . . or . . .

Grammar | Present Simple Passive

3 Complete the sentences with a verb from the box. Use the Present Simple Passive.

> give   make   play   spend   stop   take
> wash   write

1 Our pizzas _____ with fresh ingredients.
2 This book _____ by a very famous author.
3 Football is the only sport that _____ in almost every country.
4 He _____ by customs every time he enters the country.
5 I _____ to work by taxi every morning.
6 Most of our money _____ on food and drink.
7 The dirty clothes _____ in the washing machine.
8 I _____ £20 pocket money every week by my parents.

4 Make questions using the prompts and the Present Simple Passive. The answers to the quiz are below.

1 What food/Italy/know/for?
  A pizza   B hamburgers   C apples
2 What meat/not serve/to Hindus?
  A chicken   B beef   C pork
3 How much/milk/drink/in US compared to fizzy drinks?
  A 1/5   B 1/2   C 3/4
4 What complaint/hear/most often in US fast food restaurants?
  A the food is too expensive
  B there isn't enough meat in the hamburger
  C there's too much ice in the drink
5 Which animal/not eat/by Muslims?
  A cow   B sheep   C pig
6 How many teaspoons of sugar/contain/in one glass of cola?
  A 1   B 5   C 14

Answers
1A 2B 3A 4C 5C 6C

Reading

5 **a** Read the text and answer the questions.
<u>Underline</u> the best answer.

1 Jai Alai was first played in
   A Miami B Mexico C Spain and France

2 How many players play on each Jai Alai team?
   A one B two C one or two

3 What happens if the player doesn't catch the ball after one bounce?
   A the ball hits the wall
   B the other player or team gets a point
   C the other team gets seven points

4 Apart from a helmet, what do Jai Alai players wear?
   A a long shirt, trousers and a belt
   B trousers and a long belt
   C a shirt, a belt and long trousers

5 How many cestas do players use in a season?
   A 200 B 2 C 15

b Complete the sentences with the passive forms of the verbs given.

1 Jai Alai _____ to be the fastest sport in the world. (think)

2 Jai Alai _____ Pelota Vasca in Spain. (call)

3 The court which _____ for Jai Alai has three walls. (use)

4 Games _____ by one or two players on each team. (play)

5 A basket _____ to catch and throw the ball. (use)

6 The game _____ by the first player or team to score seven points. (win)

7 Helmets _____ by players to protect their heads. (wear)

Jai Alai
The fastest sport in the world?

A lot of people think that the fastest sport in the world is Jai Alai. This is a sport which originated in the Basque region of France and Spain (where it is called Pelota Vasca) and spread to the United States, Mexico and other countries. It is very popular in Florida, especially in Miami. Jai Alai players play on a court which has three walls, front, back and left. Players play individually or in doubles games like in tennis. Jai Alai players use a cesta or basket to catch and throw a very hard ball at the front wall. When one player hits the wall with the ball, the other player must catch the ball before it bounces or after one bounce. After catching the ball the player has to throw the ball back at the wall with the cesta. If the player doesn't catch the ball after one bounce, the other player or team gets a point. The first team to score seven points is the winner. Because the ball is so hard and it can travel at speeds of nearly 300 kmh, Jai Alai is dangerous. Players wear helmets to protect their heads from the ball. Apart from the helmet, players wear a coloured shirt and belt and long trousers. It can be an expensive sport as players pay about $200 for a cesta and they often use 15 cestas in one season.

Vocabulary | phrasal verbs: relationships

1 Complete the text with a verb from A and a preposition from B. Put the verbs in the correct form.

A	B
split	out
get	out with
go	apart
put	up with
ask	up
grow	over

Milly and Ahmed met in a bar. She (1) _____ him _____ and they went to the cinema the next day. After that they started (2) _____ _____ _____ each other, but things didn't go well. He was only interested in gardening and she was only interested in business, and soon they started to (3) _____ _____ . She was always working late and never had time to see him. He couldn't (4) _____ _____ _____ it, so finally they (5) _____ _____ . But he soon (6) _____ _____ it, and they stayed friends. Later she became a rich businesswoman and employed him as her gardener.

2 Underline the correct sentence.

1.
   a I split up with him.
   b I split up him.
   c I split with him up.

2.
   a I asked out her and she said yes.
   b I asked out and she said yes.
   c I asked her out and she said yes.

3.
   a We grew apart.
   b We grew apart us.
   c We grew us apart.

4.
   a I'm going with a nice man out.
   b I'm going out with a nice man.
   c I'm going nice man out with.

5.
   a I over got him.
   b I got over him.
   c I got him over.

6.
   a I hate that dog. I can't put up with.
   b I hate that dog. I can't put up with it.
   c I hate that dog. I can't put it up with.

Pronunciation | phrasal verbs: stress

3 a 🔵 24 Listen and underline the stressed words in the phrasal verbs in these sentences.

1. They split up with each other last year.
2. I wanted to ask her out but I was too scared.
3. As we got older, we grew apart.
4. We've been going out together for ages.
5. He's never really got over her.
6. I can't put up with his rude ways.

b Listen again and check your answers.

Grammar | prepositions of time

4 Put these words in the correct column.

> 2010   4:30   Christmas Day   Easter   Friday
> January   New Year's Eve   night   noon
> Sunday evening   the evening   the weekend

in	at	on

5 Correct the mistakes in five of the sentences.

1. In New Year's Day I normally have lunch with my family.
2. I usually have a rest in the afternoon.
3. The kids start school on September.
4. 'When he is retiring?' 'At 2016.'
5. What time are you getting up in the morning?
6. The plane lands at midnight.
7. At the beginning of the relationship they saw each other all the time.
8. 'When's your birthday?' 'It's on the 11th May.'
9. I start work in my new job at Monday.
10. The city is really noisy in night.

6 Complete the sentences with the correct preposition.

1 In Portugal people normally go to the beach _____ the summer.
2 In Ireland people have lunch _____ about one o'clock.
3 In America people have dinner _____ six or seven o'clock.
4 In France people sometimes go to the country _____ the weekend.
5 In Peru people eat turkey _____ Christmas Day.
6 In Mexico people celebrate with processions _____ Easter.
7 In Finland people like to have saunas _____ the winter.
8 In England people like to have tea _____ four o'clock.

Listening

7 **a** 25 Cover the audioscript. Listen and mark the sentences (1–7) true (T) or false (F).

1 Sarah got married in March last year.
2 It didn't rain on the day of the wedding.
3 Weddings in the UK are normally on Saturdays.
4 On the day of the wedding, Sarah had her breakfast after she had her hair done.
5 It took Sarah two hours to get her hair done.
6 The wedding was at three thirty.
7 Sarah was very happy at the end of the day.

AUDIOSCRIPT

I got married at the end of March this year, and it was a really lovely day. The weather was quite nice for the time of year, and we didn't have any rain to spoil our photographs! We were a bit unusual because we chose to get married on a Sunday afternoon – traditionally weddings in the UK are on a Saturday.

My day started early, at about 9 o'clock, because I had to have my breakfast and then have my hair and make-up done. My hair took more than two hours! It was boring just sitting there watching the hairdresser, but also quite nice to have some time to just relax.

The wedding itself was at 4 o'clock in the afternoon and by about 3:30 I was starting to get really nervous. Would everyone like my dress? Would I fall over as I walked down the aisle? Would my husband-to-be be late?!

Luckily none of those things happened, and everything was perfect! My face hurt from smiling by the end of the day, but I couldn't have asked for a better day – or a better husband!

b Check the audioscript for the correct answers to the false sentences.

Reading

8 Read the text and answer the questions.

A common time for weddings in Japan is the spring or autumn and they often take place in a hotel or a wedding hall. A Japanese wedding normally lasts all day and often begins with a religious ceremony. There are different religions in Japan so there are different types of weddings too: Christian, Buddhist and Shinto weddings are all common. Brides often wear traditional white kimonos with a big headpiece and the groom normally wears black.

The guests at a Japanese wedding normally dress formally. Women often wear kimonos and men wear dark suits. Usually only close family members attend the religious ceremony. At the ceremony the couple drink sake and often give each other rings. After the ceremony it is typical for the couple to change clothes before the wedding reception. Japanese wedding receptions are often big celebrations and there are sometimes hundreds of guests.

If you receive an invitation to a Japanese wedding you should reply as soon as possible. It is common for guests to give the couple a gift of money. The money is normally put inside a special envelope with the name of the person giving the present on the front.

Red and white are happy, lucky colours for weddings in Japan and sometimes the food served at the celebrations has these colours. The cutting of the cake is an important moment in Japanese wedding celebrations. Often the top parts of the cake are made of plastic or paper.

Sometimes there is a break in the reception for the bride and groom to change their clothes again. After the meal it is common for the younger guests to continue the celebrations with a band or a DJ.

1 What time of year do Japanese weddings often take place?
2 What colour do Japanese brides normally wear?
3 What do the couple drink at the wedding ceremony?
4 What do guests usually give the couple as a present?
5 What lucky colours might you see in a Japanese wedding?
6 What happens after the meal in a Japanese wedding?

8.3

Vocabulary | measurements

1 Write these numbers in words

1 56.6 kilometres per hour
2 0.068 seconds
3 2 3/4 hours
4 1,565 metres
5 63 1/2 minutes
7 3,655 centimetres
8 85 1/4 kilograms
9 1 1/2 days
10 9.96 seconds

Grammar | Past Continuous and Past Simple

2 Complete the sentences with the correct form of the verbs in brackets using Past Simple or Past Continuous.

1 I _____ (walk) past the shop when the alarm _____ (go) off.
2 He _____ (hurt) his leg while he _____ (play) rugby for his school.
3 While she _____ (work) at the hospital I _____ (get) a job at the local school.
4 She _____ (meet) her boyfriend while she _____ (study) in Italy.
5 I _____ (see) her last night when she _____ (dance) at the club.
6 He _____ (hurt) his back when he _____ (play) with his children.
7 While I _____ (read) the paper he _____ (try) to steal my telephone.
8 He _____ (get up) and _____ (make) some coffee.

3 Complete the sentences using the verbs in brackets using Past Simple or Past Continuous.

Where were you when ... ?

Dionne Grobler

I (1) _____ (watch) TV when I (2) _____ (hear) about the astronauts landing on the Moon. It (3) _____ (be) an amazing moment for the whole world. In those days many people (4) _____ (not have) a TV. I (5) _____ (call) my neighbours on the phone and they said they (6) _____ (listen) to it on the radio so I (7) _____ (invite) them to my house and we watched it on TV together.

Marsha Vygotsky

I heard the news when I (8) _____ (sit) at the table eating my breakfast. I (9) _____ (be) a musician then, in a band. The Beatles (10) _____ (not be) our heroes, but we loved John Lennon. We heard the newsreader say, 'John Lennon was killed while he (11) _____ (walk) home in New York,' and we just (12) _____ (not know) what to say.

Billy Fingleman

I (13) _____ (study) for my Masters in Politics at the time. In fact, I (14) _____ (read) a book in the university library when I (15) _____ (hear) all this noise outside. Someone said the Berlin Wall was coming down and we all (16) _____ (go) to the square and celebrated. The party (17) _____ (not finish) until 6:00 a.m.

4 Choose the correct alternative.

A strange thing (1) *was happening/happened* last summer. One night I (2) *was lying/lay* in bed. It was a stormy night and the wind (3) *was blowing/blew* very hard. I (4) *was trying/tried* to get to sleep when I (5) *was hearing/heard* a noise on the roof. To begin with, I (6) *was thinking/thought* it was the wind, but after a while the noise got louder, so I (7) *was deciding/decided* to see what it was. I (8) *was climbing/climbed* onto the roof and saw that my cat (9) *was fighting/fought* a bird. The cat (10) *was trying/tried* to catch the bird but the bird (11) *was flying/flew* a little higher than the cat and the cat couldn't catch it. When the bird (12) *was seeing/saw* me it (13) *was flying/flew* off. I (14) *was going/went* back to bed and went to sleep.

Pronunciation | was/were

5 a 🔘 26 Cover the audioscript. Listen and complete the sentences.

1 _____ it raining? _____, it _____.
2 _____ you dreaming? _____, I _____.
3 _____ they playing? _____, they _____.
4 _____ you running? _____, we _____.
5 _____ he singing? _____, he _____.

b Listen again and mark the stress. Check your answers with the tapescript.

AUDIOSCRIPT

1 Was it raining? No, it wasn't.
2 Were you dreaming? Yes, I was.
3 Were they playing? No they weren't.
4 Were you running? Yes, we were.
5 Was he singing? No, he wasn't.

Reading

6 Read the text and mark the sentences (1–6) true (T) or false (F).

1 Eric swam in the 2002 Olympic Games in Sydney.
2 The winner of the 100-metre race swam the distance in less than a minute.
3 Eric swam the minimum time before the Olympic Games.
4 Eric trained in a 50-metre pool before the Olympic Games.
5 Everyone in Equatorial Guinea thinks that Eric is hero.
6 Eric had to train in the sea after the Olympic Games.

The Slowest Swimmer in Sydney

Olympic swimmers are normally fast, very fast – but this is not always true. In 2000 Eric Mussambani represented Equatorial Guinea in the Olympic Games in Sydney. He swam in the 100 metres freestyle event. His time? One minute fifty-two seconds. The winner of the final, Pieter van den Hoogenband swam the distance in forty-seven seconds, a difference of more than a minute! But how did such a slow swimmer enter the swimming competition in the Olympic Games?

Normally swimmers have to swim a minimum time before entering the competition. However, some swimmers were allowed to compete without swimming the minimum time and Eric was one of those swimmers. He even found it difficult to complete the 100 metre race in the 50-metre Olympic pool. 'The last 20 metres was very hard,' he said. 'I didn't think I was going to be able to finish. I had never seen a 50-metre pool before. All my training was in the only pool in my country which is in a hotel. It's 20 metres long.'

For some people Eric is a hero because he shows that winning isn't the only important thing in sport. But for many people in his country he is definitely not a hero. A lot of Guineans think that he has made the country look stupid by competing so badly. 'When I got off the plane, the only people to meet me at the airport were my parents. Some people in my country are rude to me. I don't understand it. I can't even train in the hotel any more. They won't let me swim there. I have to train in the sea.'

9 | Work

Vocabulary | jobs

1 Complete each clue (1–8) with one word. Write the words in the correct places and find the key word.

1 A _____ is a person who works on a stock exchange.
2 A _____ is the money you earn for doing a job.
3 Jane didn't _____ for the job because she didn't think she would get it.
4 Some people (like police officers) have to wear a _____ in their jobs.
5 A _____ works in a hospital and helps the doctors.
6 If you do _____ work, sometimes you work in the morning or afternoons and sometimes at night.
7 A _____ worker often builds houses.
8 If you _____ , you stop working in a company because you don't want to continue working there.

2 Match the sentence halves (1–9) to (a–i).

1 One day I would like to run
2 Before I can get a new job, I need to prepare
3 He didn't like the job so he
4 If I do this job well, I might
5 As a doctor, I have to work
6 My sister had an interview
7 I have applied for a job
8 His interview went well and he was
9 Are you going to take

a long hours.
b get promoted.
c as managing director.
d offered the job.
e my own company.
f the job?
g resigned.
h my CV.
i for the job yesterday.

3 **a** Match the words in column A to the words in column B to make phrases.

A		B	
1	long	a	a job
2	high	b	a job
3	a lot of	c	work
4	shift	d	salary
5	apply for	e	training
6	be offered	f	an interview
7	get	g	hours
8	have	h	your own company
9	prepare	i	promoted
10	run	j	a CV

b Use the phrases from exercise 3a to complete the gaps in these sentences. You may need to change the tense of the verbs.

1 She _____ _____ _____ _____ from home and enjoys being the boss.
2 I go to seminars every week at work. They give us _____ _____ _____ _____ .
3 She does _____ _____ so she sometimes works at night.
4 Anna _____ _____ the job but didn't think she'd get an interview.
5 I am so tired with work. I'm working really _____ _____ at the moment.
6 Emma _____ _____ a job with a local school but decided not to take it.
7 After working in the company for years he _____ _____ and has more responsibility now.
8 I had to help Mark _____ _____ _____ as he had never written one before.
9 Martin _____ _____ _____ yesterday for a job in IBM but he said it didn't go well.
10 He's got loads of money – he's earning a really _____ _____ .

Grammar | *can, could, be able to: ability*

4 Complete the sentences using *can*, *can't*, *could* or *couldn't* and verbs from the box.

> believe   cook   finish   hear   speak
> sing   sleep   take (x2)   understand

1 My grandmother was amazing. She _____ _____ six languages fluently.
2 I _____ _____ why they haven't phoned us yet.
3 They took us to the station so we _____ _____ the train to Manchester.
4 I feel so tired because I _____ _____ last night.
5 I can play the guitar but I _____ _____ . My voice is terrible.
6 That's impossible! I _____ _____ that what you are telling me is true.
7 I've brought my camera with me, so I _____ _____ some photos.
8 When I turned the music off, I _____ _____ someone knocking at the door.
9 Tim is very fast at doing crosswords. Usually, he _____ _____ one in just three minutes.
10 My mother always cooked for me, so I _____ even _____ a plate of spaghetti when I left home.

5 Correct the mistakes in the sentences.

1 Can you speak up a little? I can hear you.
2 Samantha can't paint beautiful landscapes, but she can't paint people.
3 I want to can speak French perfectly.
4 I can't play the piano when I was younger, but now I'm not good at it.
5 She's been on a diet and now she could wear a size 8!
6 I'm sorry, but we won't could come to the wedding because we are on holiday then.
7 I can walk in these shoes. They're too big.
8 He could understand why everyone was laughing. Then he saw his photo.
9 Able you come to the party tomorrow? I need to tell Marta.
10 I'm able do maths at school, and I'm still not good at numbers.

Listening

6 a Cover the audioscript. Read the sentences (1–5). Mark them GI (good idea) or BI (bad idea).

When you write your CV …
1 write a minimum of three pages.
2 check your spelling.
3 use a computer.
4 say you have lots of qualifications, even if you do not have them.
5 give information about your junior school and all your hobbies.

b 🔘 27 Listen and check your answers.

7 Choose the correct alternative.

1 Five percent of the CVs that Melanie reads are *good/bad/OK*.
2 She thinks a CV should be *more than two pages long/exactly two pages long/two pages long or fewer*.
3 Twenty-five percent of CVs she receives contain *lies/true information/love letters*.
4 Melanie says that people lie about their *hobbies/qualifications/contact details*.
5 You should *write a new CV for each job/use the same CV for every job/write a new CV every month*.
6 A Danish woman sent some Danish *perfume/clothes/food* with her CV.
7 She *was given the job/wasn't given the job/became a chef*.

AUDIOSCRIPT

M = Melanie   I = Ivan

M: I read hundreds of CVs every week. Most of them are good. A few are excellent. And about five percent of them are terrible.
I: Really? What makes a bad CV?
M: There are a number of things. A CV should be short. No more than two pages long. I recently read a CV that was twenty pages long.
I: Unbelievable.
M: But usually the problems are quite simple.
I: What type of things?
M: Spelling mistakes. People who write their CV with a pen, not on computer. But the worst thing is that twenty-five percent of CVs are not true.
I: What do you mean?
M: People tell lies. They say they have certain qualifications and we find that they don't have them.
I: So what advice can you give about writing a CV?
M: Read the advert carefully. Learn as much as possible about the job. Then write a new CV specially for this job. Write it on a computer and only write what is important for this job.
I: Are there any imaginative or interesting ideas that work?
M: There was a woman from Denmark who applied for a job in an office. She sent some Danish food with her CV to remind us that she was from Denmark. And she got the job.

Vocabulary | work

1 Complete the text with words from the box.

> application forms   commission   CV
> employers   experience   interviewer
> managing director   qualifications   receptionist
> salary   sales rep   wage

I had been looking for a job in accounting for ages. I had filled in lots of (1) _____ and sent my (2) _____ to dozens of different companies but I was having no luck. One of the problems was that (3) _____ were looking for people with (4) _____ and this wasn't my case as I had never worked before. I did have (5) _____ as I graduated from Dundee University after studying accounting and I had done a masters course in business too. I finally got an interview with a small accounting firm in Edinburgh. When I arrived the (6) _____ told me to wait for my turn. I was very nervous and got even more nervous when I started the interview and realised that the (7) _____ was the most important person in the company – the (8) _____ ! I realised as well that they weren't really looking for an accountant but for a (9) _____ to sell their services to companies in the city. If I got the job there would be a good weekly (10) _____ as well as (11) _____ for each company I sold the services to. During the interview I worked out how much the yearly (12) _____ would be and I realised it would be a lot of money. I was desperate to get this job!

Pronunciation | changing word stress

2 a Put the words into the correct columns, depending on the syllable where the main stress is.

> applicant   application   apply   employee
> employer   ~~interview~~   interviewee
> qualification   qualify   secretarial   secretary

first syllable	second syllable	third syllable	fourth syllable
interview			

b 28 Listen and check your answers.

Grammar | adverbs of manner

3 Correct the mistakes in the sentences.

1 He completed the application form careful.
2 On her first day on the job she learned quickly the names of her colleagues.
3 You speak really well English – how long have you been studying?
4 Tim was late for the interview so ran fastly up the street.
5 They worked lately that week to be ready for the new school year.
6 She angry threw away the rejection letter.
7 I used to well play rugby when I was at school.
8 Slow he walked down the road looking at the houses.
9 Jane worked so good that her boss gave her a bonus.
10 On Monday I worked really hardly because I had to finish the report.

4 Complete these sentences with adverbs of manner so that they are true for you.

1 I speak English _____ .
2 I run _____ .
3 I sing _____ .
4 I work _____ .
5 I play football _____ .
6 I play the piano _____ .

5 Complete the text with the correct form of the word on the right.

John walked (1) _____ to school. He had forgotten to do his homework
and he was going to be in trouble with Miss McKendrick, his teacher.

sad

Miss McKendrick was a very strict teacher and she had (2) _____
told the class the day before that if anyone forgot the homework she

angry

would send them (3) _____ to the headteacher. What was worse for
John was that he sat beside Ailsa, who always did her work (4) _____

quick

and got good marks. When John got to school Ailsa was (5) _____ taking
her pens and books out of her bag.

good

'Quiet please, and sit down,' said Miss McKendrick (6) _____ . 'and put
your homework on your desks.'

careful

loud

John looked (7) _____ round. Everyone was taking out their homework.
'Excuse me, miss,' he said (8) _____ . 'I haven't done my homework.'

nervous

quiet

Reading

6 Read the text and mark the statements true (T) or false (F).

1 Jane Simmons is a sales rep.
2 Jane was asked the same questions by four interviewers.
3 Chris Ray applied for a job at a newspaper.
4 Chris had an interview with the director of the marketing department.
5 The director of the marketing department was late for the interview.
6 Jim Stevens applied for a job as a managing director.
7 Jim waited for three hours for the interview to start.
8 The interviewer wasn't very interested in Jim.
9 Jim finished the interview and left.
10 Jim's interview tells us something important about interviews.

This week our jobs expert, Neil Harrison, tells us about some bad interview experiences.

We all know that in a job interview we should try to make a good impression. We should be careful with what we wear and try not to appear nervous. Our body language can also be important. How should I sit? What should I do with my hands? But one thing we can't really do anything about is what the interviewer does. Sometimes interviewers like to ask difficult or strange questions to test an interviewee or they can even be rude. Here are some examples of some strange interviewers sent in to us by our readers.

Jane Simmons, a sales rep who went for an interview for an important sales job was introduced to five interviewers. Quite common to have an interview with more than one interviewer, she thought. What wasn't so common was for the interviewers to ask the same questions one after the other!

Chris Ray applied for a job in a marketing company which was advertised in his local newspaper. He arrived with his CV, ready for the interview with the director of the marketing department. The only problem was that the director of the marketing department didn't arrive for the interview!

Jim Stevens filled in the application form for a job in a big company as a secretary to the managing director. When he went for the interview he waited for three and a half hours before the interviewer arrived. The interviewer didn't seem too interested in Jim either. He repeated several times that this type of company didn't need Jim, but Jim needed the company. In the end, Jim got up and left the interview before it had finished. 'I realised halfway through the interview that I didn't want to work in that company.' Perhaps the example of Jim's interview tells us something important. If you go for an interview and you don't get a good impression of the company then maybe it isn't the type of company you want to work for.

9.3

Vocabulary | crime

1 Put the words from the box into the correct columns.

> arrest   commit a crime
> community service   criminal   fine
> guilty   innocent   judge   jury
> police officer   prison sentence
> steal   suspended sentence   thief
> witness

Verbs	Adjectives	People	Punishments

2 Use ten of the words and phrases from exercise 1 to complete the sentences below. You may need to change the verb forms.

1 She was given a five-year _____ and was taken to prison by the police.

2 The young man was ordered to pay a £100 _____ as his punishment.

3 The _____ ordered the people in the court to be quiet.

4 When the woman was found _____ of the crime she started to cry.

5 The _____ saw the crime and was able to describe what happened to the police.

6 His family were delighted when he was declared _____ of the crime.

7 The woman was given _____ and had to help clean the local parks.

8 The man was given a five-year _____ so he didn't go to prison.

9 After listening to all the evidence, the _____ decided that the man had robbed the bank.

10 The young man was stopped and _____ . He had been shoplifting.

3 a Complete the table using the words from the box.

> burglar   mugging   murder   pickpocket   shoplifter
> rob   thief   shoplifter

Crime	Criminal	Verb
theft	(1) robber/_____	to steal something
robbery	robber	to (2) _____ (a bank/someone)
burglary	(3) _____	to burgle a house
(4) _____	mugger	to mug someone
pick pocketing	(5) _____	to pick someone's pocket
shoplifting	(6) _____	to shoplift
(7) _____	murderer	to murder someone

b Match the verbs in exercise 3a to the definitions.

1 to take something from a shop without paying for it
_____

2 to take illegally from a house
_____

3 to take someone's money/wallet from their bag/pocket, without the person noticing
_____

4 to take something that is not yours
_____

5 to kill someone
_____

6 to attack and take something from someone (on the street)
_____

Grammar | Past Simple Passive

4 a Complete the sentences using the Past Simple Passive.

1 They sent him to prison for five years.
He _____ for five years.

2 Someone called the police.
The police _____ .

3 The police arrested the bank robber.
The bank robber _____ .

4 The judge gave him a sentence.
He _____ sentence by the judge.

5 The robber robbed the bank.
The bank _____ .

6 The jury found him guilty.
He _____ by the jury.

7 They took him to the police station.
He _____ to the police station.

b Put the sentences in the correct order.

5 Underline the correct form of the verb.

1 The old lady *was mugged/mug* in the street yesterday.

2 The murderer *arrested/was arrested*.

3 The shoplifter *was given/gave* a fine.

4 My wallet *was taken/took* by a pickpocket.

5 The bank *rob/was robbed*. They *took/was taken* £10,000.

6 The jury *decided/was decided* that he was guilty.

7 My computer *stole/was stolen* from the library.

8 My house *was burgled/burgled* last week.

9 The burglars *stole/were stolen* the DVD player.

10 The politician *was punished/punished* for not paying his taxes.

6 Correct the mistakes in five of the sentences.

1 The thief was caught with the painting in his house.

2 The judge was sent the criminal to prison for five years.

3 The crime witnessed by three different people.

4 Fourteen crimes was committed last week in the city centre.

5 The police were given a description of the criminal by the group of witnesses.

6 In five years the number of robberies was reduced by ten percent.

7 The judge was given a fine to Anna for speeding.

8 James was done his community service in local schools.

Reading

7 Read the news story about a British criminal and mark the statements true (T) or false (F).

Britain's oldest criminal has just been released from prison.

James Morton is a grandfather who has spent more than half his life in prison. However, last week, after he was released, Morton promised he wouldn't go back again. 'This job is getting too difficult,' he said. 'Everywhere you go there are TV cameras, on the street, in shops and in banks.'

Morton was first sent to prison in 1955, when he was sentenced by a judge to three years for being part of a gang that was robbing houses. The last time he was sent to prison was also for robbery, this time for robbing a bank. He was in prison for seven years for this crime. When giving him the sentence, judge Alfred Underwood told him: 'You are a career criminal. If you don't change your ways, you will die in prison.'

In total Morton has been in sixteen different prisons for fifty-four different crimes, the most serious being the last one. His favourite prison is Yorkshire Central Prison. 'The food there is great,' he said. The worst, the Greater London Prison. According to Morton it's extremely small and there is no room for proper exercise.

Outside the prison on the day of his release Morton said he wanted to spend more time with his five children and seven grandchildren. He has told them all about the dangers of a life of crime. Unfortunately they haven't all listened. His oldest grandchild was arrested by the police last year for stealing a car.

1 James Morton has spent half of his life in prison.

2 He was first sent to prison in 1955.

3 The first time he was sent to prison it was for seven years.

4 Morton has committed fifty-four different crimes.

5 He thinks the food in the Yorkshire Central Prison was very good.

6 The Greater London Prison has a lot of space.

7 Morton has seven children and five grandchildren.

8 One of Morton's children was arrested for stealing a car.

Review and consolidation 7–9

First conditional

1 Complete the sentences using the verb in brackets in the correct form.

1 If you go running everyday, you _____ better. (feel)
2 I'll come out later if I _____ this report. (finish)
3 If it _____ raining, shall we go for a walk? (stop)
4 If she _____ her exams, we'll buy her a new CD player. (pass)
5 You _____ late if you don't hurry up. (be)
6 If we _____ time to visit her, we'll phone instead. (not have)
7 Will you visit the British Museum if you _____ to London? (go)
8 If I _____ asleep now, I'll be tired tomorrow. (not fall)
9 We might go and see a film later if Pete _____ to come. (want)
10 If the course starts tomorrow, _____ you _____ to the first lesson? (come)

Gerunds and infinitives

2 Correct the mistakes in these sentences.

1 I miss to go to the beach at the weekends.
2 I didn't expect seeing you last night.
3 They decided change the time of the party.
4 The government considered to change the company law.
5 He offered helping me but I said no.
6 They seemed be happy in their new house.
7 He enjoyed to meet all my friends.
8 He doesn't want see her next week.
9 They want playing football in the park every week.
10 We can't afford buying that car.

3 Choose the correct alternative.

1 He stopped to *run/running* because the light was red.
2 He tried *catching/to catch* the ball but he dropped it.
3 You stopped to to *drive/driving* a few years ago, didn't you?
4 He remembered *playing/to play* with his brother in the holidays when he was young.
5 The driver tried *missing/to miss* the dog which ran across the road.
6 They remembered *cancelling/to cancel* the newspaper when they went on holiday.
7 I've got a very sore throat. Have you tried *to take/taking* some medicine?
8 I stopped to *play/playing* football when I had a bad injury.
9 I must remember *calling/to call* John to invite him to the party.

Present Simple Passive

4 Complete the text about a restaurant using the Present Simple Passive of the verbs in the box.

> answered   check   clean   cook   deliver
> open   pay   take

Food (1) _____ from the local markets in the mornings and this (2) _____ by the restaurant manager. The restaurant (3) _____ by the cleaners and the tables are set by the waiters. The phone starts to ring in the early afternoon and it (4) _____ by the floor manager and reservations are taken. The doors (5) _____ at 6:30 p.m. and the first customers come in. The customers are welcomed into the restaurant by the restaurant manager and they are shown to their tables. Orders (6) _____ at the tables by the waiters and these orders are taken to the kitchen. The food (7) _____ by the team of cooks who are supervised by the head chef. When the food is ready a bell rings and the food is taken to the tables by the waiters. After the meal, bills (8) _____ and the customers leave.

Past Continuous and Past Simple

5 Underline the correct verb form.

1 It *was raining/rained* when the accident *was happening/happened*.
2 When I *was coming/came* in everyone *was talking/talked* about me.
3 We *were having/had* a coffee when the stranger *asked/was asking* for Louise's number.
4 I *was travelling/travelled* in Asia when I *heard/was hearing* the news.
5 It *was/was being* a beautiful morning. The sun *was shining/shone* and the birds *were singing/sang*.
6 I *was walking/walked* through the park when I *met/was meeting* an old friend.
7 Mike *was listening/listened* to music so he *didn't hear/wasn't hearing* the telephone.
8 I *was going/went* to work when I *remembered/was remembering* I didn't have my keys.
9 As soon as I *got/was getting* home I *went/was going* to bed.
10 I *was watching/watched* television at 2:00 a.m. this morning.

can/could/be able to: ability

6 Complete the sentences using *can/can't/could/ couldn't/be able to.*

1 I'm very busy next week, so I won't _____ meet you.
2 I _____ open this door. Can you help me?
3 When I was in Kiev I _____ understand what anyone was saying.
4 She's very good at languages. When she was eight, she _____ read Greek and Latin.
5 I'm sorry, but Mr Harding _____ see you today. He's out of the office.
6 I _____ get tickets for the concert. They were sold out.
7 When I finish this course, I'll _____ to speak Japanese fluently.
8 When I was a student, I _____ afford to eat out because I was poor.
9 I'm frightened of water because I _____ swim.
10 _____ you come for a drink later?

Past Simple Passive

7 Rewrite the sentences in the Past Simple Passive. Start with the words given.

1 Someone took my bag.
My _____
2 They arrested the thief outside the bank.
The thief _____
3 People built the museum in 2001.
The museum _____
4 They met the President at the airport.
The President _____
5 Someone checked all their passports carefully.
All their _____
6 Someone told them about the delays.
They _____
7 Someone finished all the work over the weekend.
All the work _____
8 Someone invited the employees to a party.
The employees _____
9 Someone asked him to work seven days a week.
He _____
10 Someone damaged the piano when they carried it upstairs.
The piano _____

Vocabulary

8 Complete the sentences with a word from the box.

chatty   flu   handsome   hard-working
hurry   hurt   ill   skinny   sore   toe

1 I need to see a doctor about my _____ throat.
2 She doesn't eat very much and that's why she's so _____ .
3 I love George Clooney. He's so _____ .
4 She never leaves work before 9:00 p.m. She is so _____ .
5 Ouch! I just banged my _____ on the door.
6 I feel terrible. I think I've got _____ .
7 I fell down the stairs and now I've really _____ my arm.
8 I feel _____ . I hope it isn't food poisoning.
9 We spend a long time on the telephone because Meera is so _____ .
10 Can you drive a bit faster because I'm in a _____ ?

9 Put the underlined words in the correct sentences.

1 He helped her running the CV because she had never written one before.
2 He take promoted and moved to a bigger office.
3 He's been arrested his own company for years and he makes a lot of money.
4 If you want to earn for the job, please send your CV to this address.
5 He decided not to apply the job when they told him the conditions.
6 They commit long hours so they don't see each other very much.
7 We work a high salary but we have to work very hard.
8 You got a uniform in your job, don't you?
9 The witness saw him wear the crime and reported him to the police.
10 The police prepare the criminal inside the house.

Vocabulary | travel

1 **a** Put the <u>underlined</u> letters in order to make forms of transport.

Sarah *took* (take) a <u>sub</u> *bus* to the main square.

1 I prefer _____ (ride) a _____ <u>cibelyc</u> around the city. It keeps me fit.

2 We had to show our tickets before _____ (get) on the _____ <u>rinat</u>.

3 We should _____ (catch) a _____ <u>xiat</u> to the airport, or we are going to _____ (miss) the _____ <u>nealp</u>.

4 We _____ (take) a _____ <u>ryefr</u> to Robin Island. It was beautiful.

5 We _____ (go) by _____ <u>acohc</u> to Amsterdam. It was cheaper than the train.

6 You have to pay if you want to _____ (drive) a _____ <u>rac</u> in the city centre.

7 He started _____ (ride) a _____ <u>botmoreki</u> when he was fifty.

8 She _____ (get off) the _____ <u>pemdo</u> and took her helmet off.

9 They _____ (get out of) the <u>avn</u> because it was too small to carry them all.

10 The driver _____ (get into) the <u>yorlr</u> and drove off.

b Complete the sentences by putting the words in brackets into the correct form.

2 Put the <u>underlined</u> words in the correct sentences.

1 The evening train is full of <u>voyage</u> going home from work in London.

2 My <u>passengers</u> to work takes me about thirty minutes in the morning.

3 You can't take your car in there – it's a <u>journey</u> street.

4 The <u>commuters</u> complained about the food on the ship.

5 The Atlantic <u>travellers</u> took two weeks in the small yacht.

6 There are lots of <u>pedestrian</u> in India who stay in cheap hostels.

3 Use the correct type of transport to complete the comments.

www.commute.com

This week we are inviting our bloggers to tell us all about how they get to work.

Riding a (1) _____ is the best way to get about in the city. I bought my first one a few years ago and haven't looked back. Because it's not as fast as a motorbike it's not as dangerous, but you don't have to pedal like you do when riding a bike. It's also quick as you don't get stuck in the traffic.

I don't go anywhere without my (2) _____. I had a moped but it was too slow and I didn't want to get a car because getting to work would take too long with all the traffic. If the weather's bad I sometimes get a bit wet!

I have to take the (3) _____ to get across the river every day. It's very slow but I like that because it gives me time to read the paper. If the weather is good I can go outside and watch the birds on the water. I sometimes see fish too, but there aren't too many as the river is very dirty.

In my line of work I have to use my (4) _____. I need to transport things around the city. I deliver to a lot of different shops and I have a lot of space in the back. It's obviously bigger than a car, so it can be quite slow in traffic and difficult to park. But without it, I couldn't do my job.

I always ride my (5) _____ to work. I love being able to move between the traffic and I get to do some exercise every day. It's awful when it rains though!

If I need to get somewhere quick in the city, I take a (6) _____. It's more expensive than the bus but it takes me exactly where I want to go. I also like talking to the drivers. They normally have some funny stories to tell about the city.

Because of my job I have to take (7) _____ a lot. Normally I take short flights across the country because I have to visit the different offices we have. I used to like flying but now I find it really boring, especially all the waiting at the airport.

I take the (8) _____ to work most days. There's a stop around the corner from my house and the journey only takes five minutes.

Grammar | Present Perfect Simple: *just, yet, already*

4 Look at the list of things Julia needs to do before she catches her plane. Write sentences to describe what Julia has done already (✓) or hasn't done yet (✗).

Things to do:

✓1 collect plane tickets
✗2 pack clothes
✓3 find passport
✓4 change money
✓5 buy sunglasses
✓6 buy suncream
✗7 close windows
✗8 water the plants
✓9 write Erica a letter with instructions
✗10 take the cat to Erica's house

1 *She has already collected the plane tickets.*
2 _____ .
3 _____ .
4 _____ .
5 _____ .
6 _____ .
7 _____ .
8 _____ .
9 _____ .
10 _____ .

5 Put the words in the correct order to make sentences.

Jim hasn't found yet a new job.
Jim hasn't found a new job yet.

1 We've come back from Turkey just, so we haven't seen your letters.
_____

2 Fernando already has had his lunch.
_____

3 A: Have you yet read that book?
   B: Yes, I've finished it just.
_____

4 A: Have yet you been to the museum?
   B: Yes, we've been already there.
_____

5 Already I have spoken to the manager about the problem.
_____

6 A: Is Roberto still there?
   B: No. He's left just.
_____

7 It is only 9:30, but Sam already has gone to bed.
_____

6 Complete these sentences by putting *just, yet* or *already* in the correct place.

1 I've seen the report but I haven't had time to make a decision.
2 Have you seen the latest Matt Damon film?
3 I've been to Paris so I don't want to go again this summer.
4 It is only 5:00 a.m. but Sally has gone to work.
5 I've started work in the new company so I don't know many people yet.
6 Has he finished his homework? It's getting late.
7 Although he's only thirty-five he's written three books.
8 They've got back from work so they haven't started cooking dinner.

Pronunciation | showing interest

7 a 🔊 29 Listen and mark these sentences with a rising arrow (⤴) or a falling arrow (⤵), depending whether the intonation goes up or down on these phrases.

Did you see him yesterday? ⤴

1 That's fantastic!
2 What do you do on Fridays?
3 Sounds great!
4 Do you go the beach in the summer?
5 Where do you live?

b Now listen again and check your answers.

Vocabulary | greetings and gifts

1 Complete the sentences with a suitable word.

1 She _____ me on both cheeks when we said goodbye.

2 We bought some chocolates as a _____ to say thank you.

3 At the end of the concert the pianist _____.

4 We _____ at the aeroplane from the departure lounge.

5 The Prime Ministers _____ hands.

2 When would you ...

1 ... shake hands with someone?
2 ... kiss someone on the cheek?
3 ... bow?
4 ... wave to someone?
5 ... buy someone a gift?

Grammar | verbs with two objects

3 Match the sentence halves.

1 I wrote
2 He bought
3 My father taught
4 Can I offer
5 I have lent
6 I promised
7 I told
8 Did you bring
9 Dave owes

a us some chocolate from Switzerland?
b you a cup of coffee?
c me €20 for the gas bill.
d me Korean.
e him the price of the new car.
f a letter to the bank this morning.
g her my CD player, because hers is broken.
h to give him a new bicycle for his birthday.
i me some flowers, and asked me to marry him!

4 Correct the mistakes in these sentences.

1 It is a good idea to give a gift your colleagues on their birthdays.
2 They offered to him a new job with a company car.
3 Can you lend me to your car next Saturday?
4 She's sent the booking form the families.
5 The lady in reception gave to me a brochure.
6 My husband promised to me a puppy dog for my birthday.
7 The company owes money the employees.
8 I told to Julia's secret everybody in the class.
9 They showed him to the school when he arrived.
10 His mother brought to him breakfast when he was ill.

How to... | make generalisations

5 Add the words in brackets to complete the generalisations.

1 Italians love eating ice cream. (the)
_____

2 Children watch too much television. (tend to)
_____

3 Students have to get jobs in their holidays. (usually)
_____

4 Rich are getting richer every day. (the)
_____

5 People in Australia spend a lot of time outside. (generally)
_____

6 British eat a lot of roast beef. (the)
_____

7 Japanese workers don't take much holiday. (tend to)
_____

8 Teenagers don't listen to jazz or classical music. (usually)
_____

6 Correct the mistakes in the generalisations about sport in different countries.

1 Spanish men like watching generally football.
2 Americans many like sports like baseball and American football.
3 In Jamaica tend young people to do sports like athletics, especially sprinting.
4 It will be difficult to probably get a ticket to the football cup final in Brazil.
5 China wins a lot of usually gymnastics medals at the Olympics.

Listening

7 a 🔊 30 Cover the audioscript. Listen to some advice. Number the pictures in the order they are talked about.

b Listen again and complete the sentences (1–8).

1 The _____ tend to be very punctual in business.
2 For any business meeting, you should arrive _____ ...
3 If you know that you'll be late, you should _____ and tell someone about your delay.
4 When people meet for business, they _____ introduce themselves by shaking hands.
5 When you _____ , don't press too hard, or too lightly.
6 But if you need contact information, it is OK to ask a colleague for their _____ .
7 It is also OK to _____ someone your card.
8 It's important not to offer _____ or other presents as a way to help finalise a business deal.

AUDIOSCRIPT

Advice 1: The Americans tend to be very punctual in business. For any business meeting, you should arrive on time, or even early. If you know that you'll be late, you should telephone and tell someone about your delay.

Advice 2: When people meet for business, they usually introduce themselves by shaking hands. When you shake hands, don't press too hard, or too lightly. A firm handshake is best.

Advice 3: People don't always exchange business cards when they meet. But if you need contact information, it is OK to ask a colleague for their card. It is also OK to offer someone your card. But you don't have to exchange cards, as in some cultures.

Advice 4: It's important not to offer money or other presents as a way to help finalise a business deal.

Reading

8 Read the texts about Australia and Mexico and mark the sentences (1–8) A if it is true for Australia and M if it is true for Mexico.

Mexico

In general, Mexicans are happy, friendly people who like to have a good time, but that doesn't mean that there aren't things to remember when visiting the country. For example, if you are invited to a Mexican's house, it is a good idea to bring a gift like flowers or sweets. It is also a good idea to arrive late if a Mexican invites you to their home. Generally Mexicans arrive at least thirty minutes late to such an invitation. In fact if you arrive on time, it might be considered rude. If invited for dinner it is good manners to wait for the hostess to start before you start eating. When doing business with Mexicans, always arrive on time, even if your Mexican contacts arrive late. Also, Mexicans prefer face-to-face negotiations to telephone conversations or communicating by email.

Australia

In general, Australians are relaxed friendly people. It is typical for Australians to say 'G'day' when meeting someone. If you are invited to an Australian's house it is a good idea to take a present like a box of chocolates to the hostess. You might be invited to a 'barbie' (a barbecue outside in someone's garden). If you are, it is typical to take your own drinks. Your hosts might even ask you to bring your own meat! If you are invited to dinner, you should arrive on time. When you are eating your dinner, don't put your elbows on the table and keep your hands above the table. If you do business with Australians, be punctual. In business Australians can be quite direct and you should be direct too.

1 It is better to meet people face-to-face than to communicate by email.
2 Be direct if you are doing business.
3 Don't arrive on time for invitations to someone's house.
4 Take flowers as a present if you are invited to someone's home.
5 Don't start eating at dinner until the hostess starts eating.
6 Be punctual if you are invited to dinner.
7 When eating dinner, don't put your elbows on the table.

Vocabulary | *-ed* and *-ing* adjectives

1 Complete the sentences using the correct form of the adjectives from the box.

> amazed   bored   depressed   excited   frightened   relaxed
> surprised   tired

1   I was absolutely _____ by the beauty of the countryside.
2   She finds maths very _____ – she can't concentrate on it at all.
3   I had a sauna and a massage and felt really _____ afterwards.
4   The children were really _____ when all the lights went out.
5   The news about the war was really _____ .
6   The players were so _____ they fell asleep in the bus after the match.
7   The boys were so _____ about meeting David Beckham!
8   I was _____ to see Jane at the match – I didn't think she liked football.

Reading

2 Read the information about an actor and answer questions (1–6).

Gael García Bernal was born in Guadalajara, Mexico in 1978. His parents were both actors and his father was also a film director. He started acting when he was a child and and he starred in soap operas. When he was nineteen he decided to go to London to study acting. Before he went to London he had started studying philosophy but stopped because a strike closed the university. His first important film was *Amores Perros* which was directed by Mexican director Alejandro González.

Perhaps his other most important film is *The Motorcycle Diaries* where he played Ché Guevara. He had actually played Guevara before in another film in 2002. He has worked with many different directors including Pedro Almodóvar. He was nominated for a BAFTA award in 2005 for his role in *The Motorcycle Diaries*. In 2006 he was nominated for the Rising Star BAFTA, a prize for new acting talents. In 2007 he directed his first film.

1   When and where was Gael García Bernal born?
2   What jobs did his father have?
3   How old was he when he went to London to study acting?
4   Why did he stop studying philosphy?
5   How many times has García Bernal played Ché Guevara?
6   When was he first nominated for BAFTA award?

3 Match the underlined words in the text with the definitions (1–3).

1   when people don't work to protest about pay or conditions
2   a series on television or radio
3   the part an actor plays

Grammar | Past Perfect Simple

4 Choose the correct alternative.

The boy who kept walking

When thirteen-year-old Edward Daniel Sabillion arrived at New York's La Guardia Airport, he was tired. He (1) walked/had walked for thirty-seven days from Honduras across Guatemala, Mexico, Texas and Florida.

Sabillion said his mother, brother and grandfather (2) died/had died in a disaster in Honduras. He had travelled to New York to find his father, who he (3) never met/had never met before.

When Edward arrived he (4) didn't find/hadn't found his father because he had lost the address and telephone number his father (5) sent/had sent him. The boy (6) spent/had spent a day at a police station. New York Police Captain, Thomas Kelly, said, 'He (7) ate/had eaten McDonald's and had some ice cream cake.'

6 Answer the questions using the prompts.

Why didn't you recognise her?

I/not see/her for years

I hadn't seen her for years.

1 Why did you leave so early?

I/promise/to visit a friend

_____

2 Why was the house so quiet?

We/go/to bed

_____

3 Why didn't you eat with them?

I/have/my breakfast already

_____

4 Why didn't you stay in the hotel?

I/not book/a room

_____

5 Why didn't you buy the suit?

I/forgot/my credit card

_____

Pronunciation | *had/hadn't*

7 **a** Read the dialogue and <u>underline</u> the examples of *had/hadn't* if they are stressed and (circle) them if they are unstressed.

Paola: So how's your son Will doing at school?

Lucas: Well, you know how he's a bit serious and always worried about his classes. The teacher's very strict this year so he always tries to do his work as well as possible. Anyway, he got into trouble on Friday with his homework.

Paola: Why, hadn't he finished his homework?

Lucas: Well, I thought he had finished everything, but he hadn't done his maths homework. And you know that maths is the subject he has most trouble with. Anyway, when he got to school on Friday morning, the teacher hadn't started the class. So he took out his books and started to do the homework in the class. Unfortunately he had left his maths books at home. He asked one of his friends Jake for the book but Jake hadn't brought the book to school either. Anyway, the teacher saw he hadn't done his homework and gave him double homework for the next day...

b 🔵 31 Listen and check your answers.

c Listen again and check the intonation of how Lucas says *anyway*.

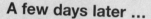

A few days later ...

The truth comes out

Yesterday, Edward Sabillion finally (8) told/had told the truth about his story. He (9) didn't walk/hadn't walked for thirty-seven days, from Honduras to New York. He already lived in the US, and had run away from home. His grandmother said she didn't know why he (10) invented/had invented this story, and she wanted him to come home.

5 Complete the sentences. Put the verbs in brackets into the correct form.

I *went* (✓) to Russia last year. I *hadn't gone* (✗) before. (go)

1 I _____ (✓) very well last night because I _____ (✗) at all the night before. (sleep)

2 I _____ (✓) lots of photos on the last day because I _____ (✗) many before. (take)

3 I was very pleased that we _____ (✓) Jessica the other day, as I _____ (✗) her for a long time. (see)

4 We _____ (✓) in a delicious restaurant. I _____ (✗) there before. (eat)

5 I _____ (✓) the new Dan Brown book because I _____ (✗) it before. (read)

Vocabulary | influence

1 Complete the sentences with the words from the box.

> adverts   celebrity   childhood   hero   media
> mentor   peers   role model

1 I think there are too many _____ on TV in the middle of programmes.

2 He had a really unhappy _____ – his brothers gave him a really bad time.

3 I think he's the typical TV _____ . He's famous for no reason.

4 When he rescued the baby from the fire he was called a _____ by all the papers.

5 I think the _____ in general has too much influence, but especially the TV.

6 Compared to his _____ he is doing very well at school.

7 She works as a _____ in a school, advising kids if they have problems.

8 He's a real _____ , you know someone the kids can imitate.

2 Match the phrases (1–6) to (a–f) to make complete expressions.

1 a natural   a by other people
2 stick   b other people to do things
3 easily influenced c leader
4 follow   d to her opinions
5 persuade   e victim
6 a fashion   f the crowd

3 Put five of the phrases from exercise 2 into the correct places in the sentences (1–5). You may need to change the form of the verbs.

1 She's a real _____ – she spends a fortune on clothes.

2 He's _____ – people always follow his lead.

3 He's not _____ . He normally does what he wants to do.

4 You won't change her mind – she always _____ .

5 They do what the others do – they always _____ .

Reading

Mentoring Programme for Schools in Auckland

Are you interested in helping children with problems at school? Do you think you have what it takes to be a mentor? If your answer to these questions is yes, read on:

Our Big Helper mentoring programme has been in operation in Auckland for ten years. Every year we are looking for adult mentors for secondary school children aged between twelve and sixteen. Each mentor is normally assigned five students to help. The areas which the students most commonly need help are: reading, writing, mathematics and social skills.

What does a mentor have to do?

Before starting, mentors have to attend a training period of a week. Once the school year starts every mentor needs to attend a group session with his/her students at least once a week. Individual tutoring may also be necessary but this would be a maximum of one hour a week. New mentors receive help from our experienced mentor team.

4 Read the advert about becoming a mentor and mark the sentences (1–6) true (T) or false (F).

1 The children the mentors work with are up to eighteen years old.

2 Mentors usually work with groups of three students.

3 Mathematics is one of the subjects that mentors help students with.

4 Mentors might have to do individual tutoring of students

5 John improved at maths after working with his mentor.

6 Richard improved at science very quickly.

7 Teachers are often good mentors.

8 If you have worked in business, you can't be a mentor.

How do students feel about mentors?

John from Ponsoby said, 'Having a mentor really helped my grades. I was never good at maths but I started passing my exams after working with my mentor.' Richard from Grey Lynn improved his science grades, 'I started to understand science for the first time in my life. It wasn't easy but I slowly started to improve.'

What skills do I need?

Almost anyone can be a mentor. Obviously people with experience in teaching can make excellent mentors, but we are also interested in hearing from people with experience in business. Basically, mentors should be positive role models for the children, so anyone who can fill this role can be a good mentor.

If you are interested in applying, please contact 09-379-8046 or send us an email at mpsa@mail.com.

Vocabulary | phrasal verbs

5 Replace the underlined words with the phrasal verbs from the box. Be careful with the tense of the verbs and the order of the words.

> bring up   come across   grow up   look after
> look up to   pick up

1 I tried to <u>raise the children</u> in a loving but strict way.
2 She <u>learnt</u> French <u>without trying</u> on her holiday in Paris.
3 She really <u>respects and admires</u> her English teacher.
4 She always <u>takes care of</u> the kids when the parents go out.
5 I <u>changed from a child to an adult</u> in Brighton during the war.
6 I <u>found</u> my old diary <u>by chance</u> when I was cleaning my room.

Grammar | *would*: past habits

6 Complete the second sentence so that it has the same meaning as the first sentence. Use *would* in your answers.

1 I used to go for walks in the country when I lived in the Lake District.

I _____ in the country when I lived in the Lake District.

2 I normally did my homework as quickly as possible when I was at primary school.

When I was in primary school, I _____ as quickly as possible.

3 When my parents went out, my elder sister used to take care of me.

My elder _____ me when my parents went out.

4 When I was waiting for my mum I often used to sit in the library reading.

I _____ the library reading when I was waiting for my mum.

5 If my dad was away, my friend's mum often took us to school.

If my dad was away, my friend's mum _____ school.

6 In the past I often listened to music on Sunday mornings.

I _____ music on Sunday mornings.

7 Find and correct the mistakes in five of these sentences.

1 I would like to play cards when I was young.
2 He would enjoy playing the piano when he was a boy.
3 I would to ask for a chocolate milkshake every Friday after school.
4 She would write poetry in her free time when she was at school.
5 They would often study together when they had exams.
6 They would know each other when they were at college.
7 They would have a good time watching films together when they first met.
8 When I was a girl, I would get up early every day to go fishing.

11.2

Vocabulary | the media

1 Put the <u>underlined</u> words into the correct sentences.

1 There's a fascinating <u>soap opera</u> about the Arctic on BBC2 this evening.
2 That <u>commercial break</u> has been on ITV for the last twenty years – I don't know how people are still interested in it.
3 I counted the <u>channels</u> in the last <u>documentary</u> in the film. There were seventeen!
4 We have forty-five different <u>drama series</u> and we still sometimes can't find anything to watch!
5 And on Channel 4 tonight there's a new three-part <u>TV adverts</u> based on life in Britain in the 60s ...

2 Write the words/phrases for the definitions (1–6). Put the words into the correct places and find the key word.

1 a computer programme which looks for files or documents from the Internet
2 a game you play on the computer
3 an advertisement which appears when you open an Internet page
4 an advertisement which you receive in your emails
5 a Internet diary which people use to write about their experiences or hobbies
6 a programme you can download from the Internet

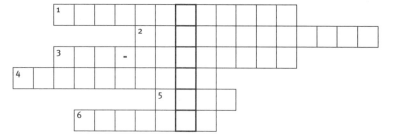

Listening

3 🔘 32 Cover the audioscript. Listen to this extract from a talk about the Rolling Stones and tick (✓) the topics mentioned in the talk.

1 The Rolling Stones were successful in the United States.
2 The Rolling Stones had less influence than the Beatles.
3 The Rolling Stones were able to change their style.
4 People imitated the Rolling Stones' look.
5 The Rolling Stones incorporated Blues sounds into their music.
6 Other bands tried to copy the Rolling Stones' sound.
7 People still listen to the Rolling Stones today.

Grammar | articles

4 Complete the sentences with *the* or nothing (–).

1 _____ computers are essential for students nowadays.
2 _____ cheapest computer programmes are the ones you get online.
3 What's _____ name of your computer science teacher?
4 This is _____ computer programme I told you about.
5 This is _____ screen that I saw in the computer shop.
6 Do you like _____ computer games?
7 _____ programme we looked at earlier is called *Cygnus 2*.
8 _____ most expensive computers are a waste of money.

5 a Read the dialogue between two friends about adverts on TV and complete the gaps with *a, an, the* or nothing (–).

A: You know I don't mind adverts, really. And sometimes there's (1) _____ great ad which can even entertain you. There's (2) _____ advert I love on TV at the moment.
B: Which one is that?
A: It's (3) _____ one for the new Forwagon car. You know, it's got David Beckham in it. I love (4) _____ images. I definitely think it's (5) _____ best ad on TV.
B: Well, I don't like (6) _____ adverts at all. (7) _____ programmes can be destroyed by too many adverts and this is happening more and more. And a lot of the time (8) _____ ads are really annoying and stick in your head. (9) _____ worst ad is the one for that new chocolate bar – it has (10) _____ really bad song. I hate it, but of course, I can't stop singing (11) _____ song.

b 🔵 33 Listen and check your answers.

6 Correct the mistakes in these sentences.

1 It's a best advert on the TV at the moment.
2 The TV these days is rubbish.
3 Have you been to a new bar in Drury Street?
4 Take a umbrella if you go out – it's going to rain.
5 Prime Minister is visiting the earthquake area at the moment.
6 Where does the Robert Jones live?
7 I bought a book and a magazine. I read a magazine on the train.
8 'Where is a toilet?' 'It's over there.'
9 The books are the best present to give to a boy for Christmas.
10 That's biggest building in the city.

How to... | use persuasive language

7 Put the sentences in the correct gaps to complete the advert.

a Designed by top computer programme designers ... tested by real students.
b Are you worried about your computer skills?
c this is the computer course you've been waiting for!
d My computer skills are terrible!!!

(1) _____

Is this how you feel about using your computer? (2) _____ If the answer to these questions is yes, then (3) _____ The Swiss Compute course deals with all areas of basic computer use. This course was designed by a team of computer scientists in Switzerland and was tested by students worldwide. Swiss Compute is effective and is incredibly easy to follow.

Swiss Compute: (4) _____ Call 902-342-566 for a free trial now!

Reading

1 Read the text about Dale Carnegie and mark the statements (1–7) true (T) or false (F).

Dale Carnegie – *influencing people*

Dale Carnegie was an American writer who wrote one of the most famous books of the twentieth century, *How to Win Friends and Influence People*.

He was born Dale Carnagey in 1888 in Missouri. His family were poor farmers and after working on the family farm milking cows as a boy, he went to study at a teaching college. After leaving college his first real job was as a salesman selling bacon. He was very successful at this but he had always wanted to be an actor so he gave up his job and moved to New York to follow this dream. It was in New York that he started giving classes in public speaking. These classes soon became very popular and he began to make a lot of money. He also started writing about ways that people can improve their self-confidence. In the 1930s his most famous book, *How to Win Friends and Influence People*, was published. The book has sold more than 15 milllion copies worldwide. In it Carnegie describes ways to get people to do what you want them to do and how to deal with people so that they feel important. Carnegie died in 1955 but his books and ideas are still very popular today and people in seventy-five countries continue to do Carnegie courses.

1 Dale Carnegie's real name was Dale Carnagey.
2 When he was a boy Carnegie milked cows on his family's farm.
3 Carnegie's first job was as a teacher.
4 Carnegie started giving classes in public speaking when he was in Missouri.
5 *How to Win Friends and Influence People* was published in 1955.
6 Carnegie died in 1958.
7 It is possible to do Carnegie courses today.

Grammar | *will* and *be going to*: decisions and plans

2 Complete the sentences using *will* and the verbs from the box in the correct form.

> arrange   call   have   open   pick up   take

1 Oh don't worry, I _____ _____ them _____ .

2 Mmm, I'm not sure ... right, OK, I _____ _____ the sushi.

3 OK, I _____ _____ the meeting with the client.

4 Wait a second, I _____ _____ the door for you.

5 I think I _____ _____ the cheaper one.

6 I _____ _____ you back in five minutes.

3 Correct the mistakes in six of these sentences.

1 I'll study medicine at university next year.

2 The exam is going to be at the end of the year.

3 'We're out of eggs.' 'I'm going to get some when I'm in town.'

4 'I haven't got any money!' 'Don't worry, I'm going to pay for the drinks.'

5 She'll do her own cooking next week because her parents are going away.

6 'I can't find my key.' 'I'm going to help you look for it.'

7 We'll stay at a small hotel when we go on holiday in the summer.

8 I'm not going to see her in London on Tuesday because she's going to be in Paris.

4 Choose the correct forms of the verbs.

1 Where *will you stay/are you going to stay* when you are in Paris?

2 *I'll pay/I'm going to pay* with my credit card if that's ok.

3 'Where would you like to sit?' '*We'll sit/We're going to sit* near the window.'

4 *He's going to study/He will study* in Europe next year.

5 ... and the children *will have/are going to have* a bottle of lemonade with their meal.

6 *They're going to live/They'll live* in Spain for a year next year.

7 'It's very dark in here.' 'Just a minute, *I'll turn on/I'm going to turn on* the light.'

8 *I'm going to do/I'll do* my driving test next summer.

Vocabulary | verb + preposition (1)

5 Complete the sentences with the correct preposition.

1 Please don't disturb him – he's revising _____ his exams at the moment.

2 He's worried _____ his daughter because she is often ill.

3 She spent $45 _____ this dress.

4 In the film she succeeded _____ changing her life.

5 I really believe _____ him. I know he is a very capable child.

6 This book appeals _____ adults and children.

7 They are very worried because she isn't responding _____ treatment.

8 She's not happy at work. She often complains _____ her boss.

6 Choose the best words to complete the text.

Just Say No!

Sally was the type of person that friends could always rely on for help. And that was because she could never say no to any favour. She helped her friends revise (1) _____ exams when she had her own studying to do. She even (2) _____ time and money on looking after her friend's dog when the friend went away. She sometimes (3) _____ about people taking advantage of her but she always worried (4) _____ saying no to people. What would they think of her? Would she lose her friends? Then, one day she saw an advertisement for a self-confidence class. She (5) _____ to the advertisement by email and was accepted for the course. At first she didn't feel like going but the more she thought about it, the more the idea of the course appealed (6) _____ her. She found the course really useful. More than anything she learned that she had to (7) _____ in herself more and not worry about what people thought of her so much. In the end it worked – she finally succeeded (8) _____ saying no more and as a result she's a lot happier now.

1	A for	B to	C in	D about
2	A talked	B gave	C used	D spent
3	A complained	B appealed	C responded	D believed
4	A to	B for	C about	D in
5	A succeeded	B answered	C spent	D responded
6	A because	B about	C for	D to
7	A complain	B believe	C think	D succeed
8	A in	B for	C why	D because

Reading

1 **a** Read the stories. Then look at the sentences. Write N (Nathan), W (woman), NW (both), or X (neither of them).

1 ☐ found a lot of money.
2 ☐ travelled on a train.
3 ☐ gave some money back.
4 ☐ stole some money.
5 ☐ ran somewhere.
6 ☐ wrote a cheque.
7 ☐ spent a lot of money.
8 ☐ called the police.
9 ☐ did something wrong more than fifty years ago.
10 ☐ won some money.

The most honest boy in Britain

1 Nathan Gittings is the most honest boy in Britain. Nathan was standing at a bus stop when he found over £10,000 in cash in two shopping bags. At first he didn't do anything. He thought that if he waited someone would return for them
5 and he would give them back. But the following day, the bags were still there. Nathan picked them up and ran home. He showed his mother what he had found and called the police. Nathan said, 'I couldn't believe it when I
10 found the money. I'd never seen that much in my life. But it wasn't mine so I knew I had to hand it in.' The Gwent police were happy and surprised at Nathan's honesty. It was
15 discovered later that the money belonged to a 'confused man'. It was his life savings.

The most honest woman in Britain

A woman who didn't pay for her train ticket returned to the
20 station and paid for it ... fifty years later. The woman, now in her sixties, said she was late when she arrived at the station in 1950. She ran into the station and jumped onto the train. If she could have bought a ticket on the train she would have but no one came to sell or check tickets that day. Fifty
25 years later the woman wrote a letter and sent a cheque to First North Western Railway Company. A single ticket is now £69 so she sent a cheque for £70. She had recently become religious and wanted to be honest about her past. The money will be given to charity.

30 *Would you be so honest if these situations happened to you?*

b What do these words refer to?

1 them (*line 4*)
   a two shopping bags
   b the bus stop
   c the police
2 it (*line 12*)
   a his home
   b the bags
   c the money
3 it (*line 20*)
   a the train
   b the station
   c the ticket

Vocabulary | money

2 Match the words and phrases with the definitions.

1 exchange rate
2 cashpoint
3 purse
4 bargain
5 currency
6 wallet
7 discount

a the money used in a country
b a thing for holding coins and paper money
c a reduction in price
d a machine where you can withdraw money
e the charge for changing money
f a thing for holding paper money
g a good price

3 **a** Mark the underlined words correct (C) or incorrect (I).

1 The best thing about living and travelling in Europe is not having to change exchange rate when you go to a different country.
2 The shop assistant gave her the change from the cashpoint.
3 She took the coins out of her purse.
4 I got a great bargain on a pair of trousers at that clothes shop yesterday.
5 Do you know what the currency is like for dollars at the moment? I have to change some euros for my trip to New York.
6 She bought her boyfriend a lovely leather wallet as a present.
7 There's a ten percent discount on all electrical goods at the moment.

b Replace the incorrect words with the correct words.

4 a Read the advice from a money expert about ways of controlling spending and saving. Complete the advice with the words from the box.

> afford borrow earn lend owe save
> spend winning withdraw

There are lots of people who can't (1) _____ luxuries and expensive things but who live well enough. True, they probably don't (2) _____ very much money for the future but they don't really have money problems. And there are also a lot of people who *do* have money problems who don't need to have these problems. Today I'm going to give some simple advice to help these people.

Well, first, try not to (3) _____ money from friends or from banks. And if you need to, try to make sure that what you pay back is never more than ten percent of what you (4) _____ in your job. And if you do (5) _____ money to someone, make sure that paying this money back is your number one priority. Whatever the amount is, you should pay this off at the beginning of the month and plan the rest of the month after this. Oh, and just as important, if you don't have much money, don't (6) _____ money to anyone! Also, try to go to the cashpoint once a week and (7) _____ the same amount of money every week. That way you won't (8) _____ more than that. And I know some people dream of (9) _____ the lottery, but that's not that likely, is it? So don't waste your money on lottery tickets!

b 🔵 34 Now listen and check your answers.

5 Complete the sentences with words from the box.

> bill change fare interest pension
> salary tax tip

1 I left a big _____ at the restaurant because the waiters were excellent.
2 My electricity _____ was really big this month because the weather was so cold.
3 I'm applying for a job with a really good _____ . If I get it I can think about buying a new house.
4 Did you know the _____ on petrol has increased? We're going to pay more now to drive the car.
5 I didn't check my _____ in the bar – that waiter charged me too much for the coffee.
6 How much is the train _____ to Edinburgh?
7 I'm paying a lot of _____ on the money I borrowed for my new car.
8 The government is going to reduce the _____ that over 65-year-olds get – I think this it terrible!

Grammar | Second Conditional

6 Put the words in the correct order using the Second Conditional. Match (1–6) to (a–f) to make sentences.

1 If I/be/better at football
2 If she/not be/so busy
3 If she/know/his number
4 If I/not already have/a dog
5 If he/eat more
6 If I/live/in Hong Kong

a get/a cat.
b not be/hungry all the time.
c have to/speak Cantonese.
d have/time to see us.
e play/in the first team.
f call/him.

7 Correct the mistakes in the sentences.

1 If I had more time, I'd to learn a new language.
2 What would you do when you lost your wallet?
3 If I would have a holiday, I'd go to Mauritius.
4 We wouldn't driven to work if we lived nearer the office.
5 She'd be here now if it is possible.
6 If you left your country, you would miss it?
7 I would sleep all morning if I would have the chance.
8 If I wasn't be so lazy, I wouldn't enjoy beach holidays.

Reading

1 Read the story and choose the best title.
- The Student With a Car.
- Paying for Accommodation as a Student.
- A Student With a Serious Debt.

A man from New Jersey who has finally passed his final university exams will not be able to start working as a lawyer. This is because John Francis, who is forty-six, owes more than half a million dollars in student loans. Yes, that's right – more than $500,000!

How did he get in debt for such a large amount of money? Well, he was studying at university for twenty-five years! In that time he studied various university courses, one of which was law. He also had to pay for accommodation all this time as a student. Part of the student debt went on a car as he had to drive to university from where he lived.

The bad news is that to start to pay back the student loan he needs a job that will pay him more than $250,000 a year. He said that he was going to do his best to find a job like this but that he thought it would be difficult. 'Who's going to give me a job like that when I don't have any experience?' he complained. 'I'm also too old for a lot of companies.' He said that he really wanted to continue studying but that he couldn't find a bank that would lend him any more money.

2 Read the story again and answer the questions (1–6).
1 How old is John Francis?
2 How much money does John Francis owe?
3 How long did he study for?
4 Why did John Francis have a car?
5 Why does he think it is going to be difficult for him to find a job?
6 Why can't Francis continue studying?

Vocabulary | money in education

3 **a** Put the phrases in the box in the correct circles to make complete expressions.

> in debt   a grant   a loan   a prize
> a scholarship   fees   a reward scheme

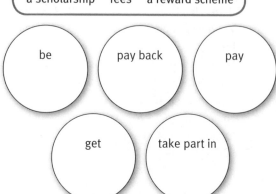

b Complete the sentences with the correct verbs from exercise 3a. You may have to change the form of the verb.
1 It took me a long time to _____ the loan that I got when I started university.
2 He was so good at tennis he _____ a sporting scholarship to study in the US.
3 She was lucky – her parents _____ her university fees for her for four years.
4 She found it really difficult to _____ a loan from the bank to study in Paris.
5 When I was eighteen I _____ a grant which helped me pay my university education.
6 She _____ several prizes at school for being top of her class.
7 Do you think it is a good idea for youngsters to _____ reward schemes at school?
8 When I was at college I _____ always in debt – I never had money to do anything!

Grammar | reported speech

4 Mick and Lola are talking. Put the sentences into reported speech. Use the verbs in brackets and *that*.
Mick: Lola, I'm hungry! (tell)
Mick told Lola that he was hungry.

1 Lola: You can go and buy some bread.
Lola _____
_____ . (tell)

2 Mick: I don't have any money.
Mick _____
_____ . (say)

3 Lola: That's nothing new.
Lola _____
_____ . (tell)

4 Mick: I'll go to the bank.
Mick _____
_____ . (say)

5 Lola: You don't have a bank account.
Lola _____
_____ . (tell)

6 Mick: I'm going to open a bank account.
Mick _____
_____ . (say)

7 Lola: You're going to need a job first.
Lola _____
_____ . (tell)

8 Mick: I'm not hungry any more.
Mick _____
_____ . (say)

5 Read the messages. What exact words did the speakers say?

John said he couldn't come tonight

'I can't come tonight.'

1   Rupesh said he would meet John at home at 6:00.
_____

2   Mary told me that her sister wasn't going to Germany.
_____

3   Rob said that my dinner was in the oven.
_____

4   Katia Scarfoni said she had been too busy to visit Renzo yesterday.
_____

5   Stephanie told me she had a meeting at 10:30.
_____

6   Dad said he had taken the keys.
_____
_____

7   Mum said we could buy some milk.
_____

8   Suleiman told me the car was ready.
_____

How to... | report back on discussions

6 Use the expressions in the box to complete the second sentences so that they have the same meaning as the first sentences.

> All of us (x2)   Most of us   None of us (x2)
> Some of us   We all agreed   We disagree about

1   The majority of the students thought that extra homework was a good idea.
   '_____ thought that extra homework was a good idea,' said the student.

2   Everybody in the department took holiday that month.
   '_____ in the department took holiday that month,' the head of department said.

3   Nobody in the team wanted to go to France that summer.
   The captain said, '_____ wanted to go to France that summer.'

4   All of the teachers said it was a good idea to buy the flat.
   '_____ that it was a good idea to buy the flat,' said the teacher.

5   The secretaries didn't agree about the holiday dates.
   '_____ the holiday dates,' said the secretary.

6   A few of the students went home early.
   '_____ went home early,' said the student.

7   Every person in the office took the afternoon off to watch the World Cup final.
   '_____ wanted to watch the game,' said Mr Jones, the boss.

8   Not one player played a good game on Friday.
   'Our whole team was terrible in Friday's game. _____ played well,' said the captain.

Vocabulary | verb + preposition (2)

1 Correct the underlined prepositions in the sentences.

1 I borrowed $10 <u>on</u> Bob for drinks.
2 I applied <u>to</u> a job in Jamaica.
3 She lent a lot of money <u>from</u> James before Christmas.
4 Do you argue <u>to</u> your brothers a lot?
5 I apologised <u>to</u> being late.
6 We waited <u>up</u> you for twenty minutes.
7 Maybe we'll have a picnic, but it depends <u>for</u> the weather.
8 I paid <u>to</u> the drinks by credit card.
9 Do you want to play <u>by</u> your friends?

2 Put the lines of the email in the correct order.

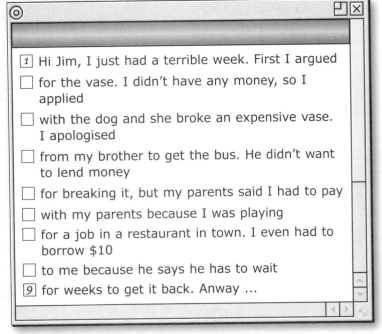

☐1 Hi Jim, I just had a terrible week. First I argued

☐ for the vase. I didn't have any money, so I applied

☐ with the dog and she broke an expensive vase. I apologised

☐ from my brother to get the bus. He didn't want to lend money

☐ for breaking it, but my parents said I had to pay

☐ with my parents because I was playing

☐ for a job in a restaurant in town. I even had to borrow $10

☐ to me because he says he has to wait

☐9 for weeks to get it back. Anway …

Grammar | both, either, neither

3 Look at photos A and B of American presidents. Mark the sentences true (T) or false (F).

1 Neither of them is wearing a tie.
2 Bill's child isn't in the photo and John's isn't either.
3 Neither of them has got a beard.
4 Both their wives are wearing a hat.
5 I don't think either of them looks unhappy.
6 Both of them have got short hair.
7 Neither of the presidents is wearing a suit.

A

4 Complete the sentences with *both*, *neither* or *either*.

The Strange Story of Two Presidents

1 Abraham Lincoln worked on a boat. John F. Kennedy also worked on a boat.

_____ of them worked on boats.

2 Lincoln was killed while he was President. Kennedy was also killed while he was President.

_____ Lincoln nor Kennedy finished their presidency.

3 Lincoln became President in 1860. Kennedy became President in 1960.

They _____ became presidents in the sixties.

4 Lincoln studied law, but didn't work as a lawyer. Kennedy also studied law, but didn't work as a lawyer.

_____ of them worked as lawyers.

5 Many white people in the south didn't like Lincoln. Many white people in the south didn't like Kennedy.

Many white southerners didn't like _____ of them.

6 After Lincoln died, Andrew Johnson (born 1808) became President. After Kennedy died, Lyndon Johnson (born 1908) became President.

Men called Johnson followed _____ of them.

7 Lincoln was killed in Ford's Theatre. Kennedy was killed in a Ford Lincoln car.

_____ of them died in Fords.

8 Kennedy saw a ghost of Lincoln in the White House (but this might not be true).

There is _____ a ghost of Lincoln in the White House or someone invented the story.

Reading

5 Read the text and mark the sentences true (T) or false (F).

Everyone knows that Americans love sports and that one of the most popular sports in America is baseball. But most people outside America don't know that a lot of Americans love collecting baseball cards – that is, cards with pictures of famous baseball players. Some baseball fans and collectors in America pay a lot of money for these cards, especially if they are old and when they are in good condition.

So how much will a collector pay for these cards? A lot of money. Some of the most expensive cards in history include one of Ty Cobb which was printed in 1914 and which sold for $100,000. Another card on the most expensive list is one of Joe Jackson from 1910. This card can be sold for between $100,000 and $200,000 if it is in good condition.

Another expensive card was one of perhaps the most famous baseball player in history, Babe Ruth. It was sold for $500,000. The card was printed in 1914 and shows Babe Ruth with the words Ruth Pitcher (the pitcher is the player who throws the ball in baseball).

But the most expensive baseball card in history is one showing Honus Wagner, a player from the beginning of the twentieth century. The card of Wagner was sold for more than two million dollars. One reason it is so valuable is that very few of these cards were made.

1 Collectors pay a lot of money for baseball cards in good condition.
2 A card of Ty Cobb printed in 1916 sold for $100,000.
3 A card of Ruth Pitcher sold for $500,000.
4 The most expensive card in history is a card of Honus Wagner.
5 Honus Wagner played baseball at the beginning of this century.
6 Not many of the Honus Wagner cards were made.

Listening

6 a 🔵 35 Cover the audioscript. Zeinab and Rob are talking about a Spanish course they have just finished. Listen and number the ideas in the order they talk about them.

Do exercises on the Internet. ☐
Read Spanish books and newspapers. ☐
Listen to CDs. ☐
Write emails to a Spanish friend. 1
Do a conversation exchange. ☐
Travel to a Spanish-speaking country. ☐

b Listen again and tick (✓) the correct sentences.

1 Zeinab wants to write emails to a friend in English.
2 Zeinab wants to visit her friend in Madrid.
3 Rob wants to do a conversation exchange with a Spanish speaker.
4 Rob and Zeinab don't like reading.
5 Zeinab wants to read poetry in Spanish.
6 They have listening CDs from their Spanish course.

AUDIOSCRIPT

R = Rob Z = Zeinab
R: Zeinab, are you going to continue with your Spanish?
Z: Oh yes, definitely.
R: How? What are you going to do?
Z: That's a good question. I've got lots of ideas. I've got a Spanish friend and we write emails to each other. We always wrote in English, but now we can write in Spanish.
R: That's great.
Z: And I'm hoping to visit her in Madrid too, so I can practise my Spanish. What about you?
R: I want to find someone to do a conversation exchange.
Z: What's that?
R: Conversation exchange? It's when you find, say, a Spanish person who wants to improve their English. Then you meet. And you speak together for half an hour in English and half an hour in Spanish.
Z: That's a good idea.
R: Yeah. I hope I can find someone at a language school.
Z: Do you read much?
R: Yeah, I like reading.
Z: I want to try reading books in Spanish.
R: What type?
Z: I'm going to try short novels or children's books. Maybe newspapers too.
R: Good idea. And there's always the Internet. There are lots of websites for language learners.
Z: That's true. And CDs too, to improve your listening.
R: Yeah, we've got the CDs from the course.

Articles and phrasal verbs

1 Complete the sentences by adding one missing word.

1   When I was in Mexico I picked a little Spanish.
2   He is brother I was telling you about.
3   When she was a child she looked up her father.
4   John Brown grew up in big, happy family.
5   Golf is best sport in the world although it's not easy to pick up.
6   I was brought a on farm, so I've always loved animals.
7   There's new TV programme on Saturday nights which we've started watching.
8   I've found a great restaurant – I came it when I went for a walk yesterday.
9   I have to after my little sister because she's feeling sick.
10 I really looked up to my elder brother when I was growing.

Present Perfect Simple: *just, yet, already*

2 Complete the gaps with *just, yet* or *already*.

1   I haven't seen the film _____ . (I'm seeing it tomorrow.)
2   She's _____ done her homework. (She did it two days earlier.)
3   Have you heard Paramour's new CD _____ ? (I expect you have.)
4   My sister has _____ had a baby boy. (She had him two hours ago.)
5   Has David finished _____ ? (The test only started ten minutes ago.)
6   I've _____ met my new boss. She's beautiful! (I met her one minute ago.)
7   We've _____ studied this topic. (We studied it weeks ago.)
8   She hasn't decided what to eat _____ . (She is very slow to choose.)
9   They've _____ opened a new school. (They opened it this morning.)
10 My cousins have _____ left. (They left five minutes ago.)

Past Perfect Simple

3 Underline the best verb form.

1   We visited Syria. We *didn't go/hadn't been* there before.
2   I went to Bill's house but he wasn't there. He *went/had gone* into town already.
3   She switched off the television and *went/had gone* to bed.
4   I wanted to listen to my personal stereo but I *left/had left* all my CDs in the flat.
5   A new secretary arrived. She *didn't work/hadn't worked* in our office before.
6   I left my job in the hospital and after that I *worked/had worked* in a factory.
7   I didn't recognise Josie because I *didn't see/hadn't seen* her for years.
8   He heard music from the flat below. The party *started/had started* already.
9   It was Dr Luber on the phone! *Did he find/Had he found* a solution to their problem?
10 I got into the car and *drove/had driven* for hours. The road was quiet.

Second conditional

4 Complete the second sentences so that they have the same meaning as the first sentences.

1   I want to buy an aeroplane. I don't have enough money.
    If I had enough money, _____ aeroplane.
2   She wants to stay here longer. She doesn't have time.
    If _____ , she would stay here longer.
3   I don't have his number so I can't call him.
    If _____ , I could call him.
4   I am very tired because I start work so early.
    If I didn't start work so early, _____ so tired.
5   John likes his job but he wants to be earn more.
    If _____ , he would be happier.
6   She finds it difficult to lose weight because she doesn't do any exercise.
    She _____ if she did more exercise.
7   We want to pay you to do a presentation at the conference.
    _____ presentation at the conference if we paid you?
8   I want to move house. I can't find anything I like.
    I _____ I could find something I liked.
9   The city is almost perfect but there are too many cars.
    If there were fewer cars, _____ perfect.
10 She wants to buy a laptop computer but they are too expensive.
    If _____ , she would buy one.

would: past habits

5 Look at the verbs in **bold** in the text. If these verbs can only be used with *used to*, write *used to* in the space before the verb. If they can be used with *would* and *used to*, write *would* before the verb.

I (1) _____ **love** going to the cinema when I was a boy. It was called the Forum and it (2) _____ **be** on the corner of a busy shopping street but it moved down a side street beside a fish and chip shop. All the boys in the local school (3) _____ **have** their birthday parties there. Before getting the tickets we (4) _____ **go** to the local sweet shop and get lots of sweets and crisps and then run into the cinema for the matinée show.

The matinée (5) _____ **be** typical kids' films like cartoons, adventure films, war films. I (6) _____ **enjoy** the war films most of all. We (7) _____ **shout** at the screen during the film and at the end of the film we (8) _____ **applaud**. The films (9) _____ **stay** in our heads after we left the cinema. I remember that for days after watching *Rocky* the boys in the street (10) _____ **pretend** they were boxers, punching the air as they went to school.

Reported speech

6 Change the sentences from direct speech to reported speech.

1 'We both like fish.'
   They told me that _____

2 'Neither of my brothers went to university.'
   I said that _____

3 'I can't dance.'
   She told me that _____

4 'It will rain later.'
   He said that _____

5 'I've lost my watch.'
   He told me that _____

6 'We don't have any money.'
   They said that _____

7 'I won't tell anyone your secret.'
   She told me that _____

8 'I'll either go to China or India for my holiday.'
   He said that _____

9 'Both of my dogs sleep all day.'
   She told me that _____

10 'Neither of my sisters has travelled much.'
   I said that _____

Vocabulary

7 Complete the sentences with the words from the box. You may need to change the tense of the verbs.

> apologise   apply   check   complain   get
> lend   pay   revise   shake   worry

1 The boy _____ for breaking the chair.

2 The businesswoman _____ hands with the delegates before the meeting.

3 She _____ very high fees when she went to the best private university in the city.

4 He was very _____ about his son's progress at school.

5 Parents often _____ about the number of children in the class.

6 She didn't _____ her change before she left the shop.

7 He tried to _____ a scholarship to study at the school but he couldn't get one.

8 They _____ for jobs at the same school because they wanted to work together.

9 Sean _____ for his exam all day but he still failed.

10 The bank _____ him money when he started his business.

8 Put the underlined letters in the correct order to make words.

1 That car is a airbgan – it's only 10,00 euros!

2 The best thing about the reryf is that you can take the car to another country.

3 I love this channel – there are no omrcmceial akebrs so you can watch a film without interruption.

4 I had a great ocldhohid. I was really happy as a boy with my family and friends.

5 'Where can I pay?' 'At the scah itll near the door.'

6 This train is always full of mutomecrs going back home from work.

7 Can you wait for me? I need to get some money out of the oishpcant.

8 There is a ten percent dcnoisut if you pay in cash.

9 'Is that a eriastpedn street?' 'Yes, cars can't go in there, only people on foot.'

10 'Which ecasrh ngeien do you use?' 'I usually use Google.'

Answer key

Unit 1 24 hours

Lesson 1.1

Vocabulary | everyday actions

1

1 j 2 h 3 d 4 g 5 b 6 c 7 i 8 e 9 f 10 a

2

1 checks 2 stay 3 take 4 have 5 go 6 have 7 read 8 have
9 listens 10 do

Reading

3a

Noon – Think about a problem, 2 p.m. – Visit the dentist, 5 p.m. – Eat
your dinner, 8 p.m. – Stretch

3b

1 T 2 F 3 T 4 T 5 F 6 T

Grammar | likes and dislikes

4a

1 hate 2 love 3 keen 4 like 5 love 6 mind 7 like 8 stand 9 quite

5

1 I'm not very keen on watching TV ... 2 She doesn't mind going to the
cinema ... 3 I'm quite keen on sports in general ... 4 He can't stand
boxing ... 5 I really like reading, ... 6 I quite like going to the theatre ...

6

1 They absolutely love going to museums. 2 He doesn't mind having
the radio on while he works. 3 She doesn't like getting up early.
4 I like eating out at weekends. 5 We quite like working together.
6 She's quite keen on gymnastics. 7 We're not very keen on dancing.
8 She really hates sports. 9 I can't stand playing chess.

Vocabulary | going out

7

1 go 2 going 3 go to 4 go 5 go 6 goes on 7 go to 8 go to

Lesson 1.2

Listening

1a

	Sleep weekdays (hours)	Sleep weekend (hours)	Insomnia (yes/no)	Alarm clock (yes/no)
Liz	about six	about ten	no	yes (two)
Paul	seven or eight	six or seven	yes (sometimes)	no (not usually)

1b

1 Liz 2 Liz 3 Paul 4 She can't sleep 5 Because she turns the first one
off and falls asleep again 6 When he has to get up very early

Vocabulary | describing your day and lifestyle

2a

1 c 2 d 3 f 4 g 5 a 6 b 7 h 8 e

2b

1 stressful 2 unusual 3 relaxing 4 lazy 5 exciting 6 busy 7 fun

Grammar | Present Simple; adverbs of frequency

3

1 doesn't know 2 finishes 3 lives 4 works 5 has 6 enjoys
7 doesn't smoke 8 does 9 doesn't work 10 spends 11 watches
12 reads 13 goes 14 does 15 doesn't cook 16 brings

4

1 What time do you have breakfast (at the weekends)? 2 Where do
they work? 3 How often does she go to the gym? 4 What do you do on
Friday night? 5 Do they ever go clubbing?

5

1 I hardly ever forget to take my books to college. 2 Jake is never late
for school in the morning. 3 We often see Pablo and Juan (Juan and
Pablo) after the game. 4 Do you always drink coffee in the mornings?
5 We sometimes visit my grandmother in France.

Pronunciation | *do/does*

6a

1 What do you do? 2 Do you like going to the cinema? 3 Do you play
football? 4 Does your teacher speak your language? 5 Does your
partner like sports? 6 Where do you live?

6b

Students' own answers.

6c

1 What do you <u>do</u>? 2 Do you like going to the cinema? 3 Do you play
football? 4 <u>Does</u> your teacher speak your language? 5 <u>Does</u> your
partner like sports? 6 Where do you live?

Lesson 1.3

Grammar | Present Continuous: now and around now

1

1 Yes, he does. No, he isn't. He's skiing. 2 Yes, they do. Yes, they are.
They're playing guitar. 3 Yes, she does. No, she isn't. She's going to
the cinema.

2

Students' own answers.

3

1 is changing 2 are starting 3 are opening 4 loves 5 are 6 It's
7 Are you working

Vocabulary | time phrases

4

1 In 2 At 3 On 4 In 5 in 6 At/On 7 In 8 On 9 At

Reading

5

1 T 2 F 3 F 4 T 5 T 6 F

Unit 2 Music

Lesson 2.1

Vocabulary | music

1

1 composer 2 single 3 soundtrack 4 concerts 5 charts

2

1 d 2 f 3 a 4 b 5 c 6 e

3

1 soundtrack 2 downloaded 3 duet 4 flop 5 lyrics

Grammar | Past Simple

4

The Queen of Pop 1 sang 2 was 3 married 4 appeared 5 won
6 sold 7 had 8 wrote
The King of Rock and Roll 1 made 2 owned 3 worked 4 married
5 sold 6 won 7 bought 8 opened

5

1 What did you have for lunch yesterday? 2 What did you do on
Saturday night? 3 What time did you get up this morning? 4 What
time did you leave the house this morning? 5 What newspaper did
you read on Sunday?

6

1 Laura met with marketing representatives. 2 She didn't take her suit
to the cleaners. 3 She rang Shane to organise the party. 4 She didn't
talk to the producers about the CD cover. 5 She checked the concert
dates. 6 She organised the accommodation for the journalists. 7 She
paid the video company. 8 She talked to the sound engineers.

Pronunciation | *-ed*

7b

/t/	/d/	/ɪd/
worked	believed	ended
finished	moved	wanted
kissed	loved	waited

7c

Students' own answers.

How to... | refer to past times

8a

a ago b In the c When d After e in f Last g later

8b

1 c 2 e 3 b 4 g 5 d 6 f 7 a

Lesson 2.2

Grammar | Present Perfect Simple: experience

1

1 I've made 2 I've performed 3 I've won 4 have you sold 5 I've sold
6 Have you 7 have you changed 8 haven't changed

2

1 haven't been 2 haven't tasted 3 haven't played 4 haven't read
5 haven't met

3

1 How many countries have you travelled to? 2 Have you ever eaten sushi? 3 How many countries have they worked in? 4 Have you ever met a famous person? 5 Has he finished his homework?
6 How many music awards has she won? 7 Have they seen the film?
8 How many world records has he broken? 9 Have you ever won a prize? 10 Have you ever played netball?

4

1 I've seen that film seven times! 2 She's been to France and Italy but she hasn't been to Greece. 3 Correct 4 I haven't found the new museum. 5 They've broken five world records in the last two years.
6 Correct 7 Correct 8 I ate there last July. 9 Correct 10 He's never met my parents.

Vocabulary | achievements

5

1 won 2 learned 3 passed 4 got 5 earn 6 gave 7 started 8 do

6

Students' own answers.

Reading

7

1 F They started in 1984. 2 T 3 F They have performed at the awards.
4 T 5 T 6 T 7 F He hit himself on the head with his guitar. 8 F Spanish videos first competed in 2005.

Lesson 2.3

Vocabulary | word families

1

1 energy 2 intelligent 3 relaxing 4 tired 5 relaxation 6 energetic
7 imagination 8 energy

Pronunciation | stress patterns

2a

1 tiring 2 energy 3 relaxing 4 energetic 5 intelligent 6 imaginative
7 imagination

Grammar | questions

3

1 Where do you work? 2 What countries have you been to?
3 Where did you see him? 4 What's your favourite music? 5 Where do you go at the weekends? 6 What are you doing at the moment?
7 Do you play a musical instrument? 8 What time did you get up on Monday?

4

1 Have you ever been to France? 2 What sort of music do you like listening to? 3 What music are you listening to at the moment?
4 How many concerts have you seen? 5 What was the last CD you bought? 6 Did you see the match yesterday? 7 Are you going to English classes at the moment? 8 Have you got an MP3 player?

5

1 Who are your biggest influences? 2 When did you start singing?
3 Have you played concerts in the US? 4 How many awards have you won? 5 Have you met any famous actors? 6 Would you like to start acting?

6

1 d 2 c 3 f 4 a 5 e 6 b

Listening

7a

	Jazz	Rock	Dance	Classical
Pavel	✓	✓	✓	✗
Helena	✓	✗	✗	✓

7b

1 into 2 listened 3 bands 4 music 5 to 6 really 7 would 8 read

Lifelong learning

8b

stress 1 example sentence 4 definition 3 part of speech 2

Unit 3 Taste

Lesson 3.1

Vocabulary | food, drink, people, kitchen equipment

1

1 H 2 I 3 J 4 L 5 K 6 E 7 F 8 A 9 G 10 B 11 C 12 D

2

1 recipe 2 traditional 3 main 4 chefs 5 menu 6 Diets 7 review
8 vegetarian

3

1 I've bought a new **cooker** for the kitchen. It cooks food really quickly.
2 The **waiter** was really angry with his boss. 3 That café is really busy – it's always full of **customers**. 4 I don't eat fruit very often but I love **plums**. 5 That **waitress** is very unfriendly. She never smiles. 6 I like sandwiches made with brown **bread**.

Listening

4a

1 She worked as a hairdresser and in a travel agency. 2 twenty-one
3 1969 4 1973 5 Cookery books 6 They sell more in supermarkets.

Reading

5

1 B 2 A 3 A 4 D 5 D 6 D

Grammar | *be going to*: future plans

6

1 We're going to win the World Cup. 2 They're going to play on the beach. 3 I'm not going to be a doctor. 4 He's going to pass his exams.
5 They're not going to get married.

7

1 Pete and Kate are going to stay in a hotel this weekend. 2 They're not going to finish the work before next week. 3 I'm not going to be at the party next week. 4 He is going to visit the Opera House in Sydney in the summer. 5 I'm not going to study French next year. 6 They're going to do a computer course next week. 7 Are you going to play football this weekend? 8 Are you going to eat at that new restaurant this weekend?

Pronunciation | connected speech (1)

8a

1 She's going to a party on Saturday night at the nightclub.

2 I'm going to have lunch on Friday at a really good restaurant.

3 I'm going to have fish and chips from a café.

4 The college trains chefs in restaurants.

5 They're going to walk around the town on Monday.

6 Did you hear about the new restaurant on Main Street?

7 They're teaching the children about food and drink.

Lesson 3.2

Vocabulary | describing food

1

1 sweet 2 spicy 3 fresh 4 grilled 5 fried 6 savoury 7 boiled 8 Raw

2

1 A 2 C 3 A 4 C 5 D 6 A 7 B 8 C

Grammar | Present Continuous: future arrangements

3
1 A: are you doing B: 'm staying ... watching 2 A: Are you cooking
B: 're having 3 A: Are you doing B: 'm not playing ... it's raining.
4 A: are you getting B: 'm not driving ... 'm taking 5 A: Are you coming
B: 're bringing 6 A: 're not going/aren't going ... B: 's going
7 aren't arriving 8 A: Are you coming B: 'm not working

4
1 're/are going 2 're/are leaving 3 'm/am visiting 4 's/is meeting
5 Are you playing 6 We're not moving 7 's having/is having
8 Are they taking 9 're/are working 10 's finishing

5
1 Are you going to the party? 2 What are you doing at two o'clock?
3 Where are you meeting Zara? 4 Are you staying at the hotel?
5 Why are you studying? 6 How are you travelling to Dublin?
7 What are you buying Oliver for his birthday? 8 How long are you
staying in Tokyo?

How to... | make arrangements

6a

Sal	Bella
Plans: staying at home	Plans (Sat): going to a concert
Reason: to study for her exams	Reason: Diane bought tickets
	Plans (Sun): going to Oxford

6b
1 On Saturday, Bella is going to a concert. 2 On Sunday, Bella is going
to Oxford.

7
Dialogue 1
(2) Hello Jim. (8) Thanks Jim. I'll tell you ... (4) Not really. I am staying
at home to study for my exams. (1) Hello Sal. It's Jim. (7) OK. I'll call
you again next week. Good luck with your exams! (6) Oh, that's really
nice of you but I don't like going out when I have to study. I'm sorry.
Perhaps another time? (3) Are you doing anything this weekend?
(5) I see. Well, why don't you come out for a drink on Saturday
evening? There's a new bar opening on the river ...
Dialogue 2
(3) What are you doing on Saturday evening? (1) Hello, Bella? It's Jim.
(7) Perfect! I can meet you on the river at 7:00 p.m. (4) Nothing. Why?
(8) 7.30 would be better for me. I'm going to Oxford on Sunday to visit
my aunt and I'm driving so I won't be back ... (5) Well, would you
like to come out for a drink, or something to eat? (2) Hello. (6) Great
idea! Oh, wait a minute. Saturday? No, I've just remembered. I'm
going to a concert on Saturday. Diane's bought some tickets to see
Coldplay. Why don't we go out on Sunday evening?

Lesson 3.3

Grammar | defining relative clauses

1a
Down 1 who 2 which 3 who 4 which 7 which 8 which
Across 5 which 6 where 9 where 10 who

1b

```
                    1
                    W
                    a
                    i
    2        3      t        4
    i        c      e        r
    c        u               r
    e   5 s  t  a  r  t  e  r
    c        t               c
    r        o               i
    e        m               p
    a        e   7           e    8
  6 m  a  r  k  e  t         l
             n               u
       9  k  i  t  c  h  e  n
             v               c
       10 c  h  e  f          h
             s
```

2
1 who 2 which 3 where 4 who 5 which 6 who 7 where

3
Students' own answers.

Vocabulary | easily confused words

4
1 receipt 2 chef 3 polite 4 sensible 5 actually 6 cooker 7 argument

Reading

5a
The Most Expensive Fast Food in the World

5b
1 two thousand dollars 2 in a restaurant in Las Vegas 3 Japan
4 two hundred euros 5 in a restaurant in New York 6 the spoon

Pronunciation | silent letters

6a
1 My <u>daughter</u> hurt her <u>knee</u>. 2 The <u>writer</u> <u>thought</u> about her book.
3 It was a cold <u>night</u> in <u>Autumn</u>. 4 There were <u>eight</u> <u>foreigners</u>.
5 <u>Could</u> you take the dog for a <u>walk</u>? 6 I <u>know</u> you're <u>wrong</u>.
7 The <u>sign</u> was <u>high</u> in the sky.

6b

Silent *g*	Silent *w*	Silent *l*	Silent *k*	Silent *n*
daughter thought night eight foreigners sign high	writer wrong	could walk	knee know	Autumn

Lifelong Learning | defining what you mean

7
1 It's something which you use for opening bottles. 2 It's the thing
that you use to dry yourself. 3 It's the stuff which you can put on
bread. 4 It's the thing which you use for changing the TV programme.
5 It's something that you can cook in. 6 It's the white stuff that you
put on your food.

Review and consolidation 1–3

Present Simple vs Present Continuous

1
1 Are you leaving 2 doesn't usually wear 3 never watch 4 is James
talking 5 Do you know 6 sometimes goes 7 am looking 8 often has
lunch 9 are you doing 10 isn't raining

2
1 What do you do? f 2 Where are you going? e 3 What is she eating? j
4 Where do they live? c 5 What time do you get home? g 6 Are you
going to the shops? a 7 What is Paul doing? i 8 Are you enjoying your
course?/Do you enjoy your course? h 9 How do you get to work? d
10 Does Jayne have a car? b

Present Simple vs Present Perfect

3
1 started 2 have made 3 sold 4 have won 5 have toured 6 have they
been 7 have always loved 8 started 9 sang 10 was 11 have always been

4
1 have lived 2 came 3 have been 4 saw 5 arrived 6 started
7 have had 8 have travelled 9 haven't found

going to and Present Continuous (for future plans/arrangements)

5
1 Are you meeting her this afternoon? 2 When are you seeing Tariq?
3 Is she playing badminton on Saturday? 4 Where are you eating?
5 Where are you going on holiday? 6 Where are you flying to?
7 What is he going to buy? 8 Are you going to take the train?

Defining relative clauses

6
1 where 2 who 3 which 4 where 5 which 6 which 7 where 8 who
7
1 Are these the keys which you can't find? 2 Do you remember the
restaurant where we had our first meal together? 3 Do you know the
name of that hotel which has double rooms for 50 euros? 4 That's the
woman who offered me her seat on the bus. 5 My sister introduced
me to a man who has his own software company.

Vocabulary

8

do	go	have	win
nothing some exercise a lot of work for charity	bowling for a walk ice skating shopping clubbing	a nap a take-away a lie-in	an award a prize

9
1 vegetarian 2 check 3 cooker 4 download 5 flop 6 time 7 earns
8 energetic

10
1 started 2 having 3 learning 4 talking 5 passed 6 take

Unit 4 Survival

Lesson 4.1

Vocabulary | collocations
1
1 interview 2 abroad 3 extreme 4 raise 5 goal 6 control 7 rely
8 strength

Grammar | comparative adjectives
2b
1 more expensive than 2 better ... than 3 more enjoyable than
4 friendlier than 5 longer 6 greater ... than 7 younger than 8 fitter
than

3
1 is bigger than 2 more dangerous than 3 as difficult as 4 isn't as
important 5 old as 6 deeper than

4a
1 F 2 T 3 F 4 T 5 F 6 T

4b
1 Martin is a bit taller than Tim. 3 Tim is much more intelligent than
James. 5 James is much fitter than Tim.

Reading
5
1 F 2 T 3 T 4 T 5 F 6 F 7 T

Vocabulary | describing people
6
1 generous 2 determined 3 intelligent 4 confident 5 motivated
6 fit 7 funny 8 reliable 9 talented 10 brave

Pronunciation | emphasising important words
7a
1 He's <u>as</u> strong <u>as</u> James. 2 She's a lot taller <u>than</u> Sheila. 3 Madrid's
a smaller city <u>than</u> London. 4 Rugby's a more dangerous sport <u>than</u>
football. 5 That book is not <u>as</u> interesting <u>as</u> the last one I read. 6 It's
<u>as</u> big <u>as</u> this house. 7 The water's a bit deeper in this pool <u>than</u> in
the small one. 8 This question is not <u>as</u> difficult <u>as</u> other ones.

Lesson 4.2

Vocabulary | survival skills
1
1 cope 2 challenge 3 myself 4 survival 5 wilderness 6 shelter

Grammar | superlative adjectives
2
1 latest 2 worst 3 oldest 4 cheapest 5 furthest 6 best 7 most
frightening 8 most popular 9 most talented

3
1 the strongest 2 the most intelligent 3 the best 4 the smallest
5 the hardest 6 the most popular 7 the tallest 8 the fittest

4
1 is the fastest 2 best food I have ever 3 of the easiest 4 the most
popular 5 most beautiful house I have 6 the smallest theatre in
7 is the heaviest 8 the best 9 the nicest 10 the most expensive

Reading
5
1 F 2 F 3 T 4 F 5 T

Lesson 4.3

Lifelong learning | British and American English
1a
line, restroom, French fries, soda, cookie, cell phone, vacation,
sidewalk, gas, check, purse, apartment, pants, chips

1b
line=queue restroom=toilet French fries=chips soda=soft drink
cookie=biscuit cell phone=mobile phone vacation=holiday
sidewalk=pavement gas=petrol check=bill purse=handbag
apartment=flat pants=trousers chips=crisps

Grammar | indirect questions
2
1 what the time is 2 where I can find an Internet café 3 where the
nearest tube station is 4 what time the next train leaves 5 if the
museum is open on Sunday 6 how much a ticket costs 7 how far it is
to the airport 8 where I can buy a phonecard

3
1 Could you tell me where the coffee shop is? 2 Do you know what
time it is? 3 Could you tell me where I can pay for the theatre?
4 Do you know what time the underground opens? 5 Can you tell me
where the bus station is? 6 Could you tell me where I can buy a ticket
for the football match?

Listening
4a
Dialogue 1 = Camden Market Dialogue 2 = Buckingham Palace
Dialogue 3 = Tate Modern Dialogue 4 = Regent's Park
Dialogue 5 = Indian restaurant, Brick Lane
Dialogue 6 = Paddington Station

4b
1 closes 2 About 3 if 4 Enjoy 5 if 6 sign 7 nearest 8 about
9 what 10 try 11 leaves 12 over

Reading
5
1 Irish 2 Two 3 Because the countryside is very green 4 1995
5 Yes, you can 6 A small hard ball used in hurling

Unit 5 Stages

Lesson 5.1

Vocabulary | stages
1
1 baby 2 toddler 3 child 4 adolescent 5 young adult 6 adult
7 middle-aged man/woman 8 retired man/woman 9 old/elderly

2
Across 3 salary 5 drive 7 get 8 have 9 retire
Down 1 place 2 graduate 4 look

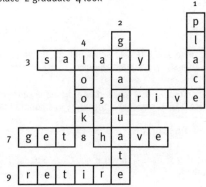

Grammar | should, have to, can: obligation and permission
3a
1 can't 2 don't have to 3 have to 4 shouldn't 5 don't have to
6 can 7 can't 8 should 9 have to 10 shouldn't 11 should 12 have to

3b
1 Diane: fashion designer 2 Karl: footballer 3 Rafael: businessman
4 Siegfried: dentist

4
1 has to 2 have to 3 can 4 can't 5 have to 6 can't 7 should
8 don't have to 9 have to 10 should

5
1 I can't swim very well. 2 He should do his homework before this afternoon. 3 Can you tell me the time? 4 I don't have to go to school on Friday afternoon. 5 They can't sing very well. 6 I should ring him tomorrow. 7 Do you play a musical instrument? 8 We have to work very hard at the moment.

Pronunciation | connected speech (2)
6a
2 ✓ 4 ✓ 6 ✓ 7 ✓ 8 ✓

How to... | exchange opinions
7
1 opinion 2 reason 3 so 4 sure 5 think 6 agree 7 right 8 sure

Lesson 5.2
Reading
1a
1 CS 2 S 3 CS 4 N 5 CS 6 CS 7 C 8 CS
1b
1 b 2 c 3 a 4 d

Grammar | Present Perfect Simple: *for* and *since*
2
for: a week, half an hour, a long time, a while, three years, ages
since: 10:30, I last saw her, then, 1996, this morning, I left school, we met
3
1 I haven't been to the city centre for ages. 2 She's lived there since 1998. 3 I've worked in the shop for a few years. 4 I haven't seen him since I was at school. 5 She's played tennis since she was a child. 6 I've known them since last year. 7 Has he played on the team for a long time? 8 He's taught at the school since 2006.
4
1 've worked 2 got 3 did you live 4 moved 5 came 6 've lived
7 've worked 8 bought
5
1 here (in China) since last 2 has lived here for 3 known John since 4 haven't seen Giorgio since 5 have played tennis since 6 have been here for 7 written poetry for

Vocabulary | friendship
6
1 lost 2 split 3 going 4 got 5 fell 6 keep 7 get 8 catch

Lesson 5.3
Reading
1a
A Long, Long Life
1b
long life, home town, feel stressed, sense of humour, ride a bike, grow old, get bored, true story, amount of money
1c
1 long life 2 home town 3 felt stressed / got bored 4 sense of humour 5 rode a bike 6 grew old 7 true story 8 amount of money

Vocabulary | habits
2
1 healthily 2 food 3 smoker 4 physical 5 active 6 stressed
7 water 8 positively

Grammar | *used to*: past habits
3a
1 Did you used to play football on Saturdays? 2 Did you used to wear a uniform at school? 3 Did you used to get good marks? 4 Did you used to eat fast food? 5 Did you used to travel for work?
3b
a Yes, I to used get good marks in my exams when I was at school.
b No, I didn't use to wear one. c No, I only used to eat fruit and vegetables. d No, I never used to travel for work. e Yes, I used to play every Saturday.
3c
1 e 2 b 3 a 4 c 5 d

Listening
4a
1 T 2 T 3 F 4 T 5 F 6 F

Unit 6 Places
Lesson 6.1
Vocabulary | places and geographical features
1
1 capital 2 situated 3 destinations 4 remains 5 natural 6 landscape
7 population 8 spaces
2
1 island 2 river 3 mountain 4 forest 5 beaches 6 lake 7 Sea 8 bay
9 peninsula 10 coast 11 cliffs

Grammar | *will*, *may* and *might*: prediction
3
1 I might finish it later if I have time. 2 He won't win the game tomorrow if he plays like that. 3 correct 4 I might go to the cinema this evening if there's a good film on. 5 I'm sure they will join the company next year. 6 correct 7 I might start work early on Thursday. 8 correct
4
1 I'll see 2 I'll go 3 Will you stay 4 I'll finish 5 I'll get 6 I do 7 I visit
8 I'll send

Pronunciation | contractions: *will*
5a
1 It'll be 2 They'll eat 3 I'll have 4 She'll be 5 you'll pass 6 He'll be

Reading
6a
1 S 2 WA 3 WA 4 S 5 WA
7
1 NI 2 T 3 F 4 F 5 T 6 NI
8
1 e 2 c 3 b 4 f 5 d 6 a

Lesson 6.2
Listening
1
1 B 2 A 3 J 4 J 5 J 6 B 7 A

Grammar | countable and uncountable nouns
2
1 any 2 many 3 any 4 much 5 a little 6 a lot of 7 a few 8 a lot of
9 some
3
1 some 2 little 3 a lot of 4 few 5 any 6 many 7 little 8 much 9 few
4
1 many 2 many 3 a few 4 a bit 5 some 6 some 7 many 8 a few
9 many 10 much

Vocabulary | describing a place
5a
1 romantic 2 unspoilt 3 peaceful 4 idyllic 5 crowded 6 noisy
7 relaxing 8 exciting 9 beautiful 10 impressive 11 pleasant 12 wild
5b
1 noisy 2 exciting 3 impressive 4 crowded 5 peaceful 6 unspoilt
7 beautiful 8 relaxing 9 wild 10 pleasant 11 romantic 12 idyllic
5c
Students' own answers.

Pronunciation | diphthongs

6a

/eɪ/	/aɪ/	/ɔɪ/	/əʊ/	/aʊ/	/ɪə/	/eə/	/ʊə/
pl<u>a</u>ce	ex<u>ci</u>ting	unsp<u>oi</u>lt	l<u>o</u>cal	cr<u>ow</u>ded	disapp<u>ear</u>	<u>a</u>rea	t<u>ou</u>r

Lesson 6.3

Vocabulary | urban environment

1
1 leisure centre 2 book shop 3 restaurant 4 nightclub 5 hospital
6 cinema 7 art gallery 8 school

2
Across 1 college 3 theatre 4 bar
Down 6 bus stop 7 station 8 café 9 library 10 museum

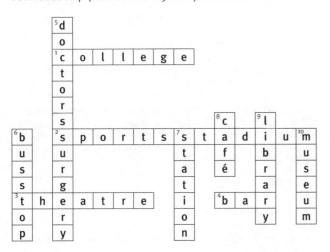

Grammar | too, too much/many, (not) enough

3
1 too 2 too many 3 enough 4 too much 5 too 6 enough 7 too much
8 too many

4
1 too loud 2 tall enough 3 too … suitcases 4 enough money
5 too crowded 6 too small

5
1 too tired 2 hard enough 3 too much time 4 too expensive
5 too many hamburgers 6 good enough 7 too long 8 too many
people 9 too busy 10 old enough

Reading

6b
1 F 2 NI 3 F 4 F 5 T 6 F 7 NI

Review and consolidation 4–6

Comparative and superlative adjectives

1
1 hotter 2 more dangerous 3 the largest 4 younger 5 more
interesting than 6 the most romantic 7 smaller 8 the best 9 lazier
10 the prettiest 11 kinder 12 the fastest

Indirect questions

2
1 Can you tell me what time the train leaves? 2 Do you know where
the pharmacy is? 3 Do you know where I can buy a bus ticket?
4 Can you tell me what time the film starts? 5 Do you know where the
information desk is? 6 Can you tell me how I can open this gate?
7 Can you tell me the time? 8 Can you tell us how to get to the
station? 9 Do you know where she works? 10 Can you tell me how
much the stamps are?

should, can, have to: obligation and permission

3
1 should buy 2 don't have to 3 has to do 4 Can I go 5 shouldn't arrive
6 can't drive 7 have to read 8 should eat 9 I have to 10 can fly

used to and Present Perfect with for and since

4
1 I used to eat junk food but I have been much healthier since last
year. (c) 2 She used to be good at the guitar but she hasn't played

for two years. (e) 3 We didn't use to like each other when we were
children but we've been friends for the last few months. (a) 4 Mum
and Dad used to travel a lot but they haven't had a holiday since
2005. (d) 5 I didn't use to cook much pasta but I've eaten a lot of it
since I went to Italy. (b)

will, may and might with too, too much/many, (not) enough

5
1 will, too many 2 might, too 3 will, enough 4 will, too much 5 will,
enough 6 enough, won't 7 might, too 8 won't, too 9 won't, too
10 too much, won't

Countable and uncountable nouns

6
1 I don't have much money left this month. 2 We need some orange
juice for breakfast. 3 Have you got any oranges? 4 We don't know
many people in the area yet. 5 There isn't any modern equipment on
the farm. 6 Do you have any trees in your garden? 7 In the morning
the garden gets a bit of sunshine. 8 Normally there are only a few
people in the café at lunchtime. 9 Have you got much time after
dinner to do your homework? 10 Can I have some water please?

Vocabulary

7
1 graduated 2 get 3 earn 4 get 5 learn 6 cope 7 control 8 think
9 achieved

8
1 adolescent 2 brave 3 coast 4 destination 5 elderly 6 fit 7 gallery
8 healthily 9 idyllic 10 junk 11 keep 12 leisure 13 motivated
14 nightclub 15 on 16 peninsula 17 remains 18 shelter 19 toddler
20 unspoilt 21 vegetables 22 wild 23 young

Unit 7 Body

Lesson 7.1

Vocabulary | appearance

1
1 waist 2 shoulder 3 elbow 4 wrist 5 ear 6 nose 7 back 8 knee
9 finger 10 forehead 11 ankle 12 eye 13 mouth 14 hair

2a
1 b 2 d 3 e 4 a 5 c

2b
1 put on weight 2 get stressed 3 looks like 4 went on a diet
5 physical appearance

3
1 b 2 c 3 f 4 e 5 g 6 d 7 a

Grammar | First Conditional

4
1 we'll celebrate with a party. 2 we'll stay in and eat a pizza. 3 I'll go
to the bank and get some. 4 I'll buy you a copy for your birthday.
5 we'll talk about it later. 6 there won't be any left. 7 will you come?

5
1 see/will you 2 don't come/will be 3 will be/don't call
4 don't leave/'ll miss 5 won't be/go 6 find/'ll tell 7 'll be/aren't
8 don't sleep/won't feel

6
1 If Pete does lots of exercise, his muscles will get stronger.
2 If Shaune does yoga, She'll/She will feel happier. 3 Their skin will
look better if they drink lots of water. 4 They'll/They will feel more
relaxed if they have massages every day. 5 If Shaune eats salads for a
week, she'll/she will lose weight. 6 They won't/will not feel so tired if
they sleep for ten hours a day. 7 If they don't/do not eat junk food for a
week, they will feel healthier. 8 They'll be/will be less stressed if they
don't/do not think about work. 9 If Pete loses more weight he'll/he will
have more energy. 10 If they stay at the health farm too long, they will
be/feel healthier but (be) poorer!

7
1 If I pass the exam, I'll get the place at university I want. 2 I'll ring you
tomorrow, if I see him. 3 We'll get a new car if he gets a new job.
4 They won't be happy if they don't go to the party. 5 You'll see her
on the news if you turn on the TV at 9.00. 6 You won't be cold if you
take your jacket. 7 I can use the computer programme if you teach me.
8 If you see him tomorrow, will you tell him the news?

Pronunciation | intonation in conditional clauses
8
1 I'll do it tomorrow if I have time.

2 We'll take you home by car if you stay for the match.

3 They will be very angry if they see the rubbish on the floor.

4 If you get to work late, you'll have to leave later.

5 If we take the train, we'll be there by five thirty.

Lifelong learning | remembering words
9
Possible answers: 1 c 2 e 3 a 4 d 5 b

Lesson 7.2
Vocabulary | personality
1
1 ambitious 2 chatty 3 organised 4 sensitive 5 hard-working
6 open 7 unreliable 8 reserved

Pronunciation | schwa /ə/ on unstressed syllables
2a
1 happy to talk about feelings 2 make lots of lists and plans
3 are easy to talk to and talk a lot 4 don't talk about feelings or
problems 5 really want to be successful 6 not easily annoyed or
worried by things 7 don't like work or physical activity

Grammar | gerunds and infinitives
3
1 to think 2 talking 3 meeting 4 to take 5 working 6 to change
7 moving 8 to find 9 to tell 10 seeing
4
1 to learn 2 looking at 3 to read 4 to do 5 to try 6 to tell 7 to change
8 listening 9 to understand 10 to travel 11 winning 12 to say
5
1 I am hoping to meet the artist at the exhibition. 2 I miss seeing my
friends and family. 3 I expect you to be here at 9 o'clock. 4 correct
5 He has decided to take a week off work. 6 We avoided telling you
earlier because of your exams. 7 You can't afford to go out every
night. It's too expensive. 8 I promised to go to her house this
evening. 9 I want to tell you what happened. 10 correct

Reading
6b
1 F 2 T 3 T 4 F 5 F 6 F
6c
1 The right hand shows personality. 4 The heart line normally finishes
under the little finger. 5 Often the head line joins with the life line.
6 The fate line represents things the person cannot control.

Lesson 7.3
Vocabulary | illness
1
1 sore wrist 2 sore eyes 3 high temperature 4 feel sick 5 neck hurts
2
1 Have you got an aspirin? I've got a terrible headache. 2 I can't eat
anything. I feel sick. 3 You don't look well. Have you got / Do you
have a high temperature? 4 I ate too much chocolate and now I've got
a stomachache. 5 I'm going to try acupuncture for my backache.
6 I don't feel very good. I've got a cold. 7 I'm staying at home. I've got
the flu.

How to ... | give and respond to advice
3
a 4 b 2 c 3 d 1 e 5

Grammar | stop, try, remember with infinitives
4
1 being 2 to study 3 to stop 4 feeling 5 going
5
1 Correct 2 Why don't you try taking some honey and butter in hot
milk? 3 I feel terrible. I can't stop coughing! 4 correct 5 Stop going to
the gym if you've hurt your leg! 6 I know you've got a lot of work but
try to take a break every few hours.
6 Students' own answers

Listening
7a
1 C
7b
1 acupuncture 2 energy 3 Japanese 4 ask 5 massage 6 press
7 backaches 8 headaches 9 1/an hour 10 No 11 more

Unit 8
Lesson 8.1
Vocabulary | speed
1
1 j 2 f 3 e 4 g 5 a 6 c 7 d 8 i 9 h 10 b
2
1 in 2 behind 3 up with 4 on 5 down 6 up

Grammar | Present Simple Passive
3
1 are made 2 was written 3 is played 4 is stopped 5 am taken
6 is spent 7 are washed 8 am given
4
1 What food is Italy known for? 2 What meat is not served to Hindus?
3 How much milk is drunk in the US compared to fizzy drinks? 4 What
complaint is heard most often in US fast food restaurants? 5 Which
animal is not eaten by Muslims? 6 How many teaspoons of sugar are
contained in one glass of cola?

Reading
5a
1 C 2 C 3 B 4 C 5 C
5b
1 is thought 2 is called 3 is used 4 are played 5 is used 6 is won
7 are worn

Lesson 8.2
Vocabulary | phrasal verbs: relationships
1
1 asked ... out 2 going out with 3 grow apart 4 put up with 5 split up
6 got over
2
1 a 2 c 3 a 4 b 5 b 6 b

Pronunciation | phrasal verbs: stress
3a
1 split up with 2 ask her out 3 grew apart 4 going out 5 got over
6 put up with

Grammar | prepositions of time
4

in	at	on
January	the weekend	Sunday evening
the evening	4.30	Christmas Day
2010	noon	New Year's Eve
	night	Friday
	Easter	

5
1 On New Year's Day ... 2 correct 3 The kids start school in
September. 4 'When he is retiring?' 'In 2016.' 5 correct 6 correct
7 correct 8 correct 9 I start work in my new job on Monday.
10 The city is really noisy at night.
6
1 in 2 at 3 at 4 at 5 on 6 at 7 in 8 at
7
1 F Sarah got married in March this year. 2 T 3 T 4 F She had her
breakfast after she had her hair done. 5 F It took Sarah more than two
hours to get her hair done. 6 F The wedding was at four o'clock. 7 T
8
1 In the spring or autumn. 2 White 3 Sake 4 Money 5 Red and white
6 Younger guests continue the celebrations with a band or a DJ.

Lesson 8.3

Vocabulary | measurements

1
1 fifty-six point six 2 nought point nought six eight/zero point zero six eight 3 two and three-quarters 4 one thousand, five hundred and sixty-five 5 sixty-three and a half 6 three thousand, six hundred and fifty-five 8 eighty-five and a quarter 9 one and a half 10 nine point nine six

Grammar | Past Continuous and Past Simple

2
1 was walking, went 2 hurt, was playing 3 was working, got 4 met, was studying 5 saw, was dancing 6 hurt, was playing 7 was reading, tried 8 got up, made

3
1 was watching 2 heard 3 was 4 didn't have 5 called 6 were listening 7 invited 8 was sitting 9 was 10 weren't 11 was walking 12 didn't know 13 was studying 14 was reading 15 heard 16 went 17 didn't finish

4
1 happened 2 was lying 3 was blowing 4 was trying 5 heard 6 thought 7 decided 8 climbed 9 was fighting 10 was trying 11 was flying 12 saw 13 flew 14 went

Pronunciation | was/were

5a and b
1 Was it <u>raining</u>? <u>No</u>, it <u>wasn't</u>. 2 Were you <u>dreaming</u>? <u>Yes</u>, I <u>was</u>. 3 Were they <u>playing</u>? <u>No</u> they <u>weren't</u>. 4 Were you <u>running</u>? <u>Yes</u>, we <u>were</u>. 5 Was he <u>singing</u>? <u>No</u>, he <u>wasn't</u>.

Reading

6
1 F 2 T 3 F 4 F 5 F 6 T

Unit 9

Lesson 9.1

Vocabulary | jobs

1
1 stockbroker 2 salary 3 apply 4 uniform 5 nurse 6 shift 7 construction 8 resign

¹s	t	o	c	k	b	r	o	k	e	r
²s	a	l	a	r	y					
		³a	p	p	l	y				
⁴u	n	i	f	o	r	m				
		⁵n	u	r	s	e				
⁶s	h	i	f	t						
⁷c	o	n	s	t	r	u	c	t	i	o	n
⁸r	e	s	i	g	n					

2
1 e 2 h 3 g 4 b 5 a 6 i 7 c 8 d 9 f

3a
1 g long hours 2 d high salary 3 e a lot of training 4 c shift work 5 a/b apply for a job 6 a/b be offered a job 7 i get promoted 8 f have an interview 9 j prepare a CV 10 h run your own company

3b
1 runs her own company 2 a lot of training 3 shift work 4 applied for 5 long hours 6 was offered 7 got promoted 8 prepare a CV 9 had an interview 10 high salary

Grammar | can, could, be able to: ability

4
1 could speak 2 can't understand 3 could take 4 couldn't sleep 5 can't sing 6 can't believe 7 can take 8 could hear 9 can finish 10 can't ... cook

5
1 Can you speak up a little? I can't hear you. 2 Samantha can paint beautiful landscapes, but she can't paint people. 3 I want to be able to speak French perfectly. 4 I could play the piano when I was younger, but now I'm not good at it. 5 She's been on a diet and now she can wear a size 8! 6 I'm sorry, but we won't be able to come to the wedding because we are on holiday then. 7 I can't walk in these shoes. They're too big. 8 He couldn't understand why everyone was laughing. Then he saw his photo. 9 Can you/Are you able (to) come to the party tomorrow? I need to tell Marta. 10 I'm wasn't able to do Maths at school, and I'm still not good at numbers.

Listening

6a
1 BI 2 GI 3 GI 4 BI 5 BI

7
1 bad 2 two pages long or fewer 3 lies 4 qualifications 5 write a new CV for every job 6 food 7 was given the job

Lesson 9.2

Vocabulary | work

1
1 application forms 2 CV 3 employers 4 experience 5 qualifications 6 receptionist 7 interviewer 8 managing director 9 sales rep 10 wage 11 commission 12 salary

Pronunciation | changing word stress

2a

first syllable	second syllable	third syllable	fourth syllable
<u>in</u>terview <u>app</u>licant <u>qual</u>ify <u>sec</u>retary	ap<u>ply</u> em<u>ploy</u>er	appli<u>ca</u>tion emplo<u>yee</u> secre<u>tar</u>ial	intervie<u>wee</u> qualifi<u>ca</u>tion

Grammar | adverbs of manner

3
1 He completed the application form carefully. 2 On her first day on the job she quickly learned the names of her colleagues. 3 You speak English really well – how long have you been studying? 4 Tim was late for the interview so ran quickly up the street. 5 They worked late that week to be ready for the new school year. 6 She angrily threw away the rejection letter. 7 I used to play rugby well when I was at school. 8 Slowly he walked down the road looking at the houses. 9 Jane worked so well that her boss gave her a bonus. 10 On Monday I worked really hard because I had to finish the report.

4
Students' own answers.

5
1 sadly 2 angrily 3 quickly 4 well 5 carefully 6 loudly 7 nervously 8 quietly

Reading

6a
1 T 2 F 3 F 4 T 5 F 6 F 7 F 8 T 9 F 10 T

Lesson 9.3

Vocabulary | crime

1

verbs	adjectives	people	punishments
steal commit a crime arrest	innocent guilty	police officer criminal thief jury judge witness	suspended sentence fine prison sentence community service

2
1 prison sentence 2 fine 3 judge 4 guilty 5 witness 6 innocent 7 community service 8 suspended sentence 9 jury 10 arrested

3a
1 thief 2 rob 3 burglar 4 mugging 5 pickpocket 6 shoplifter 7 murder

3b
1 shoplift 2 burgle 3 pickpocket 4 steal 5 murder 6 mug

Grammar | Past Simple Passive

4a

1 He was sent to prison for five years. 2 The police were called.
3 The bank robber was arrested by the police. 4 He was given a sentence by the judge. 5 The bank was robbed by the robber. 6 He was found guilty by the jury. 7 He was taken to the police station.

4b

5 2 3 7 6 4 1

5

1 was mugged 2 was arrested 3 was given 4 was taken 5 was robbed, took 6 decided 7 was stolen 8 was burgled 9 stole 10 was punished

6

1 correct 2 The judge sent the criminal to prison for five years.
3 The crime was witnessed by three different people. 4 Fourteen crimes were committed last week in the city centre. 5 correct
6 correct 7 The judge gave a fine to Anna for speeding. 8 James did his community service in local schools.

Reading

7

1 F 2 T 3 F 4 T 5 T 6 F 7 F 8 F

Review and consolidation 7–9

First conditional

1

1 will feel 2 finish 3 stops 4 passes 5 will be 6 don't have 7 go
8 don't fall 9 wants 10 will ... come

Gerunds and infinitives

2

1 I miss going to the beach at the weekends. 2 I didn't expect to see you last night. 3 They decided to change the time of the party.
4 The government considered changing the company law. 5 He offered to help me but I said no. 6 They seemed to be happy in their new house. 7 He enjoyed meeting all my friends. 8 He doesn't want to see her next week. 9 They want to play football in the park every week. 10 We can't afford to buy that car.

3

1 running 2 to catch 3 driving 4 playing 5 to miss 6 to cancel
7 taking 8 playing 9 to call

Present Simple Passive

4

1 is delivered 2 is checked 3 is cleaned 4 is answered 5 are opened
6 are taken 7 is cooked 8 are paid

Past Continuous and Past Simple

5

1 was raining, happened 2 came, was talking 3 were having, asked
4 was travelling, heard 5 was, was shining, were singing 6 was walking, met 7 was listening, didn't hear 8 was going, remembered I didn't have my keys. 9 got, went 10 was watching

can/could/be able to: ability

6

1 be able to 2 can't 3 couldn't 4 was able to/could 5 can't
6 couldn't 7 be able to 8 couldn't 9 can't 10 Can

Past Simple Passive

7

1 My bag was taken. 2 The thief was arrested outside the bank.
3 The museum was built in 2001. 4 The President was met at the airport. 5 All their passports were checked carefully. 6 They were told about the delays. 7 All the work was finished over the weekend.
8 The employees were invited to a party. 9 He was asked to work seven days a week. 10 The piano was damaged when they carried it upstairs.

Vocabulary

8

1 sore 2 skinny 3 handsome 4 hard-working 5 toe 6 flu 7 hurt
8 ill 9 chatty 10 hurry

9

1 prepare 2 got 3 running 4 apply 5 take 6 work 7 earn 8 wear
9 commit 10 arrested

Unit 10

Lesson 10.1

Vocabulary | travel

1

1 riding, bicycle 2 getting, train 3 catch, taxi, miss, plane 4 took, ferry
5 went, coach 6 drive, car 7 riding, motorbike 8 got off, moped 9 got out of, van 10 got into, lorry

2

1 commuters 2 journey 3 pedestrian 4 passengers 5 voyage 6 travellers

3

1 moped 2 motorbike 3 ferry 4 van 5 bicycle 6 taxi 7 planes 8 bus

Grammar | Present Perfect Simple with *just*, *yet*, *already*

4

1 She has already collected the plane tickets. 2 She hasn't packed her clothes yet. 3 She has already found her passport. 4 She has already changed some money. 5 She has already bought some sunglasses.
6 She has already bought suncream. 7 She hasn't closed the windows yet. 8 She hasn't watered the plants yet. 9 She has already written a letter for Erica. 10 She hasn't taken the cat to Erica's house yet.

5

1 We've just come back from Turkey, so we haven't seen your letters.
2 Fernando has already had his lunch. 3 A: Have you read that book yet? B: Yes, I've just finished it. 4 A: Have you been to the museum yet? B: Yes, we've been there already. 5 I have already spoken to the manager about the problem. 6 A: Is Roberto still there? B: No. He's just left. 7 It is only 9:30, but Sam has already gone to bed.

6

1 I've just seen the report but I haven't had time to make a decision.
2 Have you seen the latest Matt Damon film yet? 3 I've already been to Paris so I don't want to go again this summer. 4 It is only 5:00 a.m. but Sally has already gone to work. 5 I've just started work in the new company so I don't know many people yet. 6 Has he finished his homework yet? It's getting late. 7 Although he's only thirty-five he's already written three books. 8 They've just got back from work so they haven't started cooking dinner.

Pronunciation | showing interest

7a

1 That's fantastic!

2 What do you do on Fridays?

3 Sounds great!

4 Do you go the beach in the summer?

5 Where do you live?

Lesson 10.2

Vocabulary | greetings and gifts

1

1 kissed 2 present/gift 3 bowed 4 waved 5 shook

2

Students' own answers.

Grammar | verbs with two objects

3

1 f 2 i 3 d 4 b 5 g 6 h 7 e 8 a 9 c

4

1 It is a good idea to give your colleagues a gift on their birthdays.
2 They offered him a new job with a company car. 3 Can you lend me your car next Saturday? 4 She's sent the booking form to the families.
5 The lady in reception gave me a brochure. 6 My husband promised me a puppy dog for my birthday. 7 The company owes money to the employees. 8 I told Julia's secret to everybody in the class. 9 They showed him the school when he arrived. 10 His mother brought him breakfast when he was ill.

How to... | make generalisations

5

1 The Italians love eating ice cream. 2 Children tend to watch too much television. 3 Students usually have to get jobs in their holidays.
4 The rich are getting richer every day. 5 People in Australia generally spend a lot of time outside. 6 The British eat a lot of roast beef.
7 Japanese workers don't tend to/tend not to take a lot of holidays.
8 Teenagers don't usually listen to jazz or classical music.

6

1 Generally Spanish men like watching football. 2 Many Americans like sports like baseball and American football. 3 In Jamaica young people tend to do sports like athletics, especially sprinting. 4 It will probably be difficult to get a ticket to the football cup final in Brazil. 5 China usually wins a lot of gymnastics medals at the Olympics.

Listening

7a

1 b 2 d 3 a 4 c

7b

1 Americans 2 on time 3 telephone 4 usually 5 shake hands
6 card 7 offer 8 money

Reading

8

1 M 2 A 3 M 4 M 5 M 6 A

Lesson 10.3

Vocabulary | *-ed* and *-ing* adjectives

1

1 amazed 2 boring 3 relaxed 4 frightened 5 depressing 6 tired
7 excited 8 surprised

Reading

2

1 1978 in Mexico (Guadalajara) 2 actor and film director 3 nineteen
4 Because a strike closed the university 5 twice 6 2005

3

1 strike 2 soap opera 3 role

Grammar | Past Perfect Simple

4

1 had walked 2 had died 3 had never met 4 didn't find 5 had sent
6 spent 7 ate 8 told 9 hadn't walked 10 had invented

5

1 slept/hadn't slept 2 took/hadn't taken 3 saw/hadn't seen
4 ate/hadn't eaten

6

1 I'd/had promised to visit a friend 2 We'd/had gone to bed.
3 I'd/had my breakfast already. 4 I hadn't booked a room.
5 I'd/had forgotten my credit card.

Pronunciation | *had/hadn't*

7a

Paola: So how's your son Will doing at school?
Lucas: Well, you know how he's a bit serious and always worried about his classes. The teacher's very strict this year so he always tries to do his work as well as possible. Anyway, he got into trouble on Friday with his homework.
Paola: Why, <u>hadn't</u> he finished his homework?
Lucas: Well, I thought he (had) finished everything, but he <u>hadn't</u> done his maths homework. And you know that maths is the subject he has most trouble with. Anyway, when he got to school on Friday morning, the teacher <u>hadn't</u> started the class. So he took out his books and started to do the homework in the class. Unfortunately he (had) left his maths books at home. He asked one of his friends Jake for the book but Jake <u>hadn't</u> brought the book to school either. Anyway, the teacher saw he <u>hadn't</u> done his homework and gave him double homework for the next day ...

Unit 11

Lesson 11.1

Vocabulary | influence

1

1 adverts 2 childhood 3 celebrity 4 hero 5 media 6 peers 7 mentor
8 role model

2

1 c 2 d 3 a 4 f 5 b 6 e

3

1 fashion victim 2 a natural leader 3 easily influenced by other people
4 sticks to her opinions 5 follow the crowd

Reading

4

1 F 2 F 3 T 4 T 5 T 6 F 7 T 8 F

Vocabulary | phrasal verbs

5

1 I tried to bring the children up/bring up the children in a loving but strict way. 2 She picked up French on her holiday in Paris. 3 She really looks up to her English teacher. 4 She always looks after the kids when the parents go out. 5 I grew up in Brighton during the war. 6 I came across my old diary when I was cleaning my room.

Grammar | *would*: past habits

6

1 I would go for walks in the country when I lived in the Lake District. 2 When I was in primary school, I would do my homework as quickly as possible. 3 My elder sister would take care of me when my parents went out. 4 I would sit in the library reading when I was waiting for my mum. 5 If my dad was away, my friend's mum would often take us to school. 6 I would listen to music on Sunday mornings.

7

1 I used to like to play cards when I was young. 2 He used to enjoy playing the piano when he was a boy. 3 I would ask for a chocolate milkshake every Friday after school. 4 correct 5 correct. 6 They used to know each other when they were at college. 7 They used to have a good time watching films together when they first met.
8 correct.

Lesson 11.2

Vocabulary | the media

1

1 documentary 2 soap opera 3 TV adverts, commercial break
4 channels 5 drama series

2

1 search engine 2 computer game 3 pop-up advert 4 direct mail
5 blog 6 podcast

s	e	a	r	c	h	e	n	g	i	n	e		
					c	o	m	p	u	t	e	r	g	a	m	e
		p	o	p	-	u	p	a	d	v	e	r	t
d	i	r	e	c	t	m	a	i	l			
					b	l	o	g				
		p	o	d	c	a	s	t				

Listening

3

1 ✓ 2 ✓ 3 ✗ 4 ✗ 5 ✓ 6 ✓ 7 ✓

Grammar | articles

4

1 – 2 The 3 the 4 the 5 the 6 – 7 The 8 The

5a

1 a 2 an 3 the 4 the 5 the 6 – 7 – 8 the 9 The 10 a 11 the

6

1 It's the best advert on TV at the moment. 2 TV these days is rubbish. 3 Have you been to the new bar in Drury Street? 4 Take an umbrella if you go out – it's going to rain. 5 The Prime Minister is visiting the earthquake area at the moment. 6 Where does Robert Jones live? 7 I bought a book and a magazine. I read the magazine on the train. 8 'Where is the toilet?' 'It's over there.' 9 Books are the best present to give to a boy for Christmas. 10 That's the biggest building in the city.

How to... | use persuasive language

7

1 d 2 b 3 c 4 a

Lesson 11.3

Reading

1

1 T 2 T 3 F 4 F 5 F 6 F 7 T

Grammar | *will* and *be going to*: decisions and plans

2
1 I'll/I will pick (them) up. 2 I'll/I will have 3 I'll/I will arrange
4 I'll/I will open 5 I'll/I will take 6 I'll/I will call

3
1 I'm going to study medicine at university next year. 2 correct
3 'We're out of eggs.' 'I'll get some when I'm in town.' 4 'I haven't got
any money!' 'Don't worry, I'll pay for the drinks.' 5 She's going to do
her own cooking next week because her parents are going away.
6 'I can't find my key.' 'I'll help you look for it.' 7 We're going to stay
at a small hotel when we go on holiday in the summer. 8 correct

4
1 are you going to stay 2 I'll pay 3 We'll sit 4 He's going to study
5 will have 6 They're going to live 7 I'll turn on 8 I'm going to do

Vocabulary | verb + preposition (1)

5
1 for 2 about 3 on 4 in 5 in 6 to 7 to 8 about

6
1 A 2 D 3 A 4 C 5 D 6 D 7 B 8 A

Unit 12

Lesson 12.1

Reading
1a
1 N 2 W 3 NW 4 X 5 NW 6 W 7 X 8 N 9 W 10 X
1b
1 a 2 c 3 c

Vocabulary | money
2
1 e 2 d 3 b 4 g 5 a 6 f 7 c
3a
1 I 2 I 3 C 4 C 5 I 6 C 7 C
3b
1 currency 2 cash till 5 exchange rate
4a
1 afford 2 save 3 borrow 4 earn 5 owe 6 lend 7 withdraw
8 spend 9 winning
5
1 tip 2 bill 3 salary 4 tax 5 change 6 fare 7 interest 8 pension

Grammar | Second Conditional
6
1 If I was better at football, I would play in the first team. 2 If she
wasn't so busy, she would have time to see us. 3 If she knew his
number, she would call him. 4 If I didn't already have a dog, I would
get a cat. 5 If he ate more, he wouldn' t be hungry all the time. 6 If I
lived in Hong Kong, I would have to speak Cantonese.
7
1 If I had more time, I'd learn a new language. 2 What would you do if
you lost your wallet? 3 If I had a holiday, I'd go to Mauritius.
4 We wouldn't drive to work if we lived nearer the office. 5 She'd be
here now if it was possible. 6 If you left your country, would you miss
it? 7 I would sleep all morning if I had the chance. 8 If I wasn't so
lazy, I wouldn't enjoy beach holidays.

Lesson 12.2

Reading
1
A Student with a Serious Debt.
2
1 forty-six 2 more than $500,000 3 twenty-five years 4 to drive to
university 5 because he doesn't have any experience 6 because he
can't find a bank to lend him any more money

Vocabulary | money in education
3a
be: in debt pay back: a loan get: a grant, a scholarship, a prize
take part in: a reward scheme pay: fees
3b
1 pay back 2 got 3 paid 4 get 5 got 6 got 7 take part in 8 was

Grammar | reported speech

4
1 Lola told Mick that he could go and buy some bread. 2 Mick said
that he didn't have any money. 3 Lola told Mick that that was nothing
new. 4 Mick said that he would go to the bank. 5 Lola told Mick that
he didn't have a bank account. 6 Mick said that he was going to open
a bank account. 7 Lola told Mick that he was going to need a job first.
8 Mick said that he wasn't hungry any more.

5
1 I'll meet John at home at 6:00. 2 My sister isn't going to Germany.
3 Your dinner is in the oven. 4 I was too busy to visit Renzo yesterday.
5 I have a meeting at 10:30. 6 I have taken the keys. 7 You can buy
some milk. 8 The car is ready.

6
1 Most of us 2 All of us 3 None of us 4 We all agreed 5 We disagree
about 6 Some of us 7 All of us 8 None of us

Lesson 12.3

Vocabulary | verb + preposition (2)
1
1 from 2 for 3 to 4 with 5 for 6 for 7 on 8 for 9 with
2
(1) Hi Jim, I just had a terrible week. First I argued (2) with my parents
because I was playing (3) with the dog and she broke an expensive
vase. I apologised (4) for breaking it, but my parents said I had to pay
(5) for the vase. I didn't have any money, so I applied (6) for a job in
a restaurant in town. I even had to borrow $10 (7) from my brother to
get the bus. He didn't want to lend money (8) to me because he says
he has to wait (9) for weeks to get it back. Anway ...

Grammar | *both*, *either*, *neither*
3
1 F 2 F 3 T 4 F 5 T 6 T 7 F
4
1 Both 2 Neither 3 both 4 Neither 5 either 6 both 7 Both 8 either

Reading
5
1 T 2 F 3 F 4 T 5 F 6 T

Listening
6a
Do exercises on the Internet 5 Read Spanish books and newspapers 4
Listen to CDs 6 Write emails to a Spanish friend 1 Do a conversation
exchange 3 Travel to a Spanish-speaking country 2
6b
1 F 2 T 3 T 4 F 5 F 6 T

Review and consolidation 10–12

Articles and phrasal verbs
1
1 When I was in Mexico I picked up a little Spanish. 2 He is the brother
I was telling you about. 3 When she was a child she looked up to her
father. 4 John Brown grew up in a big, happy family. 5 Golf is the best
sport in the world although it's not easy to pick up. 6 I was brought
up a on farm, so I've always loved animals. 7 There's a new TV
programme on Saturday nights which we've started watching.
8 I've found a great restaurant – I came across it when I went for a
walk yesterday. 9 I have to look after my little sister because she's
feeling sick. 10 I really looked up to my elder brother when I was
growing up.

Present Perfect Simple: *just, yet, already*
2
1 yet 2 already 3 yet 4 just 5 already 6 just 7 already 8 yet 9 just
10 just

Past Perfect Simple
3
1 hadn't been 2 had gone 3 went 4 had left 5 hadn't worked
6 worked 7 hadn't seen 8 had started 9 Had he found 10 drove

Second conditional

4

1 I would buy an 2 she had more time 3 I had his number 4 I wouldn't be 5 John earned more 6 would find it easier to lose weight 7 Would you do a 8 would move house if 9 the city would be 10 laptop computers weren't so expensive/computers were cheaper

would: past habits

5

1 used to 2 used to 3 used to 4 would 5 used to 6 used to
7 would 8 would 9 would 10 would

Reported speech

6

1 they both liked fish 2 neither of my brothers had been to university
3 she couldn't dance 4 it would rain later 5 he had lost his watch
6 they didn't have any money 7 she wouldn't tell anyone my secret
8 he would either go to China or India for his holiday 9 both of her dogs slept all day 10 neither of my sisters had travelled much

Vocabulary

7

1 apologised 2 shook 3 paid 4 worried 5 complain/complained
6 check 7 get 8 applied 9 revised 10 lent

8

1 bargain 2 ferry 3 commercial breaks 4 childhood 5 cash till
6 commuters 7 cashpoint 8 discount 9 pedestrian 10 search engine

Pearson Education Limited
Edinburgh Gate
Harlow
Essex CM20 2JE
England
and Associated Companies throughout the world.

www.pearsonlongman.com

© Pearson Education Limited 2011

First published 2011

ISBNs:
9781408267370
New Total English Pre-Intermediate Workbook with Key and Audio
CD Pack
9781408267387
New Total English Pre-Intermediate Workbook without Key and
Audio CD Pack

Set in MetaPlusBook-Roman
Printed in Spain by Graficas Estella

Design: Pearson Education

Photo acknowledgements

The publisher would like to thank the following for their kind permission to reproduce their photographs:

(Key: b-bottom; c-centre; l-left; r-right; t-top)

Alamy Images: Buzzshotz 73
Corbis: ColorBlind Images/Blend Images 45, Jutta Klee 49, Parrot Pascal 34, Turba 48
Mary Evans Picture Library: 32t
Getty Images: Sean Gallup 68, Hulton Getty 81, Mike Marsland 16, Stuart McClymont 35b, Time & Life Pictures 74t
iStockphoto: Justin Sneddon 21t, Martina Vignatelli 38b, Jacob Wackerhausen 7b
Pearson Education Ltd: Gareth Boden 15b, 19b, Gareth Boden 15b, 19b, Corbis 5b, Michael Duerinckx 64b, Rob Judges 26b, Naki Kouyioumtzis 52b, MindStudio 7t, 30t, 30tc, MindStudio 7t, 30t, 30tc, MindStudio 7t, 30t, 30tc, Stockbyte 5t
Photolibrary.com: 81A Productions 4b, Suzanne Long 37b, Jeremy Woodhouse 20, Chu Yong 41
Press Association Images: Ulf Palm 55b, Stephen Savoia 80
PunchStock: Ruberball 13
Rex Features: 10t, 10b, 59b, 72b, 75, Neale Haynes 51, Frank Sutton 32b, Warner Br/Everett 38t
Shutterstock: 19t, 29b, 71t, Yuri Arcurs 7c, Chris Howey 39, Evgeny Murtola 37t, Antonio Jorge Nunes 15t, Rafael Ramirez Lee 36, RoxyFer 30b, Sielemann 30bc, StockLite 77b, Wavebreakmedia ltd 56b
South Wales Echo: 76
Thinkstock: 19c, Hemera 33b, 54c, Hemera 33b, 54c, Istockphoto 54t, 54b, Istockphoto 54t, 54b

Cover images: Photolibrary.com: George Hammerstein

All other images © Pearson Education

Picture Research by: Rebecca Sodergren

Every effort has been made to trace the copyright holders and we apologise in advance for any unintentional omissions. We would be pleased to insert the appropriate acknowledgement in any subsequent edition of this publication.